BASTARD AND CONQUEROR
WILLIAM

Story
MINIAC

Illustrations
BORCH

OREP
EDITIONS

OREP Éditions, Zone tertiaire de Nonant, 14400 BAYEUX
Tel. : 02 31 51 81 31 - **Fax :** 02 31 51 81 32
E-mail : info@orepeditions.com - **Web :** www.orepeditions.com

Extracts from the 11th century Bayeux Tapestry reproduced thanks to special authorisation from the Town of Bayeux.
Pages 70-72 are taken from *William the Conqueror in 58 stages* by Annie Fettu and *The Bayeux Tapestry, the Comic Strip*
by Gilles Pivard, both published by Orep editions and courtesy of the authors.

Graphic design: OREP
"William" logo, lettering and layout: David Thouroude
Translation: Heather Inglis
ISBN: 978-2-8151-0234-6

Legal deposit: 1st quarter 2017

IN HIS FATHER'S SHADOW

AT LAST!

HERE HE COMES!

IT WAS IN FALAISE, IN THE DUCHY OF NORMANDY, THAT I WAS BORN...

...VERY PROBABLY IN FEBRUARY 1027.

OUÏÏNN!! OUÏÏNN!! OUÏÏNN!!

OUÏINN!! OUÏINN!!

YOUR WILLIAM IS A FINE BOY, HERLEVA!

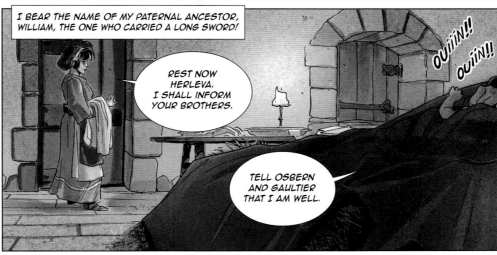

I BEAR THE NAME OF MY PATERNAL ANCESTOR, WILLIAM, THE ONE WHO CARRIED A LONG SWORD!

REST NOW HERLEVA. I SHALL INFORM YOUR BROTHERS.

TELL OSBERN AND GAULTIER THAT I AM WELL.

OUÏIN!! OUÏIN!!

NINE MONTHS EARLIER, ON A WARM DAY IN THE SPRING OF 1026, IN FALAISE. A NOBLE HORSEMAN WAS RETURNING FROM A HUNTING TRIP.

HE WAS MY FATHER, ROBERT, THE DUKE OF NORMANDY'S YOUNG BROTHER.

HIS ELDER BROTHER, RICHARD, HAD BECOME DUKE UPON THE DEATH OF THEIR FATHER THE SAME YEAR.

AT THE VAL DE L'ANTE FOUNTAIN...

HE WAS STRUCK BY CUPID'S ARROW...

AS SOON AS MY FATHER SET EYES ON HER...

SHE WAS MY MOTHER, AND HER COMPLEXION WAS AS DELICATE AS A ROSE IN BLOOM.

I LOVE YOU!

SHE MUST HAVE BEEN 16 OR 17. JUST LIKE MY FATHER.

THE FOLLOWING NIGHT, THE CASTLE OFFERED A HAVEN FOR A NIGHT OF LOVE.

THEY SAY THAT, THE NEXT MORNING, MY MOTHER WOKE FROM A DREAM, A DREAM OF A HUGE TREE THAT GREW FROM HER STOMACH, CASTING ITS SHADOW OVER NORMANDY...

AND OVER ENGLAND.

FATHER, I WISH TO MARRY HERLEVA!

A CHRISTIAN WEDDING IS IMPOSSIBLE. WHO IS THAT MAN FULBERT, HER FATHER?

HE IS BUT AN HONOURABLE BURGHER! THE DUKE'S SON CANNOT MARRY A COMMON MAN'S DAUGHTER!

THEN I SHALL MARRY HER IN THE DANISH MANNER[1]!

JUST LIKE OUR ANCESTORS, LIKE ROLLO AND POPPA!

SHE WILL BE MY "FRILLA". SO WHAT IF HERLEVA CANNOT CLAIM THE PRIVILEGES OF RANK! SHE CARES NOT, FOR SHE LOVES ME!

SHE ALSO GAVE HIM A DAUGHTER, MY YOUNGER SISTER ADELAIDE, BORN AROUND 1030.

WE WERE TWO CHILDREN BORN OUT OF WEDLOCK BLESSED BY THE CHURCH, TWO BASTARDS...

SOON, RELATIONS BETWEEN MY UNCLE RICHARD AND MY FATHER BECAME SOUR.

MY FATHER REFUSED TO FULFIL HIS OBLIGATIONS AS A VASSAL TOWARDS HIS ELDER BROTHER AND HE REBELLED AGAINST HIM.

MY FATHER, WHO HAD INHERITED EXMES[2], WANTED FALAISE. ENTRENCHED WITHIN THE CITY WALLS, THE DUCAL ARMY BESIEGED HIM.

DOMINATED DESPITE THE MARSHES THAT PREVENTED THE SIEGE ENGINES FROM APPROACHING, HE EVENTUALLY SURRENDERED.

[1] MARRIAGE DANISH-STYLE, OR MORE DANICO, REFERS TO A FORM OF POLYGAMY PRACTICED BY THE VIKINGS ESTABLISHED IN NORMANDY. THE CHILDREN BORN FROM SUCH UNION WERE "BASTARDS" BUT COULD CLAIM THEIR PATERNAL SUCCESSION.
[2] EXMES WAS, AT THE TIME, AN EXTREMELY IMPORTANT LOCALITY IN NORMANDY.

HOWEVER, RICHARD III GRANTED HIM HIS PARDON AND, IN 1027, THEIR RECONCILIATION WAS SEALED BY MEANS OF A BANQUET ON THE 6TH OF AUGUST...

BUT MY UNCLE RICHARD SUDDENLY DIED UPON HIS RETURN FROM THE MEAL.

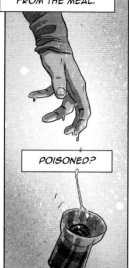

POISONED?

"BUT WHO BENEFITS FROM THE CRIME? ROBERT!" AS MALICIOUS GOSSIP WOULD HAVE IT.

HENCE, AT THE AGE OF SEVENTEEN, MY FATHER BECAME DUKE...

...MY COUSIN NICOLAS, MY UNCLE'S ILLEGITIMATE SON, WAS SENT TO FÉCAMP TO SERVE AS A MONK.

THE RICHARDIDES, THE BARONS WHO DESCENDED FROM DUKES RICHARD I AND II[3], NATURALLY CHALLENGED MY FATHER'S LEGITIMACY.

WITH MY MOTHER'S INTERVENTION, AND IN THE INTERESTS OF HER OWN FAMILY MEMBERS, MY GRANDFATHER FULBERT BECAME THE DUKE'S VALET.

AFTER HIS BROTHER'S DEATH, MY FATHER IS SAID TO HAVE OFFERED MY MOTHER A REAL WEDDING.

AT THE AGE OF THIRTY, THE PENNILESS LORD HERLUIN OFFERED LOYAL SUPPORT TO MY FATHER. HE MARRIED MY MOTHER.

TOGETHER, THEY QUICKLY HAD TWO SONS...

KLANG!!

FIRSTLY ODO, THEN HIS YOUNGER BROTHER ROBERT, AND A GIRL, MURIEL.

[3] RICHARD I, DUKE FROM 942 TO 996. RICHARD II, DUKE FROM 996 TO 1026.

MY FATHER WAS A SKILLED STRATEGIST AND OFFERED SUPPORT TO THE YOUNG KING HENRY I[4] OF FRANCE, AGAINST THE KING'S YOUNG BROTHER ROBERT. SUPPORT THAT WAS TO EARN HIM THE VEXIN COUNTY.

AN INHERITANCE THAT WAS TO BE A SOURCE OF CONFLICT FOR MY FATHER WHO LIKED TO GOVERN WITH AN IRON FIST!

MY FATHER WAS QUICK TO RECOVER LAND FROM THE RICH ABBEYS AND VAST CHURCHES TO OFFER THEM TO YOUNG NOBLEMEN. THIS LED TO CONFLICT WITH HIS POWERFUL UNCLE, ROBERT II, ARCHBISHOP OF ROUEN.

DURING THE SIEGE OF ÉVREUX IN 1027-1028, ROBERT II NEGOTIATED, PREFERRING EXILE WITH THE KING OF FRANCE, WHILST OPENLY CURSING NORMANDY. MY FATHER BOWED TO THE CIRCUMSTANCES AND REINSTATED HIS UNCLE...

AS MY ADVENTUROUS FATHER INCESSANTLY WAGED WAR AGAINST THE RECALCITRANT BARONS TO MAINTAIN HIS VULNERABLE DUCHY,

YAOUU!!

I TOOK MY FIRST PONY RIDES IN FALAISE.

HE CRUSHED REBELLIONS, IN PARTICULAR THE ONE LED BY HIS VASSAL WILLIAM TALVAS, THE CONSPIRATOR FROM BELLÊME.

AFTER THE SIEGE OF ALENÇON IN 1027...

WALK!

TALVAS WAS HUMILIATED BY MY FATHER BEFORE HIS OWN VASSALS!

THERE'S NO TURNING BACK! I AM GOING TO JERUSALEM TO MEDITATE, BARE-FOOTED, ON THE TOMB OF JESUS CHRIST!

HOWEVER, IN JANUARY 1035, MY FATHER SUDDENLY ANNOUNCED TO THE BISHOPS...

PENITENCE!

I MUST SET OFF ON PILGRIMAGE TO THE HOLY LAND!

ROBERT, BE REASONABLE, THE DUCHY IS SO FRAGILE!

WHAT WILL BECOME OF IT HERE, WITH NO SOVEREIGN?

ONE DOES NOT ALWAYS RETURN FROM SUCH A JOURNEY!

BUT I AM AWARE OF THE DANGER. TO REASSURE YOU MY FRIENDS, I WILL CONVENE THE DUCHY'S GREAT NOBLEMEN TO AN OFFICIAL GATHERING.

[4] HENRY I, KING FROM 1031 TO 1060.

THE POWERFUL ABBEY OF FÉCAMP, THE LAST RESTING PLACE OF THE DUKES RICHARD I AND II, WAS UNDER THE ABBOTSHIP OF JEAN DE RAVENNE SINCE 1028.

NOBLEMEN, I HAVE CONVENED THIS ASSEMBLY...

FOR I HAVE NO HEIR ...

...HERE IS MY SON ...

AT THE AGE OF JUST SEVEN, I WAS RATHER INTIMIDATED BY THE SIGHT OF ALL THOSE PEOPLE.

SHOULD I NOT RETURN FROM THE HOLY LAND, MY SON WILL BE YOUR LORD. I ENTREAT YOU, MY VASSALS, TO CONSIDER HIM AS YOUR LEADER!

WITH GOD'S HELP, HE WILL BECOME STRONG!

IN NO TIME, HE WILL DEFEND YOU AND GOVERN YOU.

HE WILL BE PLACED UNDER THE KING OF FRANCE'S PROTECTION.

ALL THE BARONS ACCEPTED THE DUKE'S DECISION.

I WAS ROBERT'S ONLY SON.

BUT I WAS SO YOUNG

AND ILLEGITIMATE ...

HENRY OF FRANCE, NEED I REMIND YOU OF THE FAVOURS I HAVE EXTENDED? I ASK YOU TO ACCEPT MY SON'S HOMAGE.

I ACKNOWLEDGE HIM AS MY VASSAL AND OFFER HIM MY PROTECTION!

MY UNCLE[5] ALAN, DUKE OF BRITTANY, I ENTRUST YOU WITH THE REGENCY OF THE DUCHY. NEVER FORGET YOUR OWN EXPERIENCE...

AS A YOUNG DUKE, YOU ALSO SUFFERED FROM A DIFFICULT CHILDHOOD. UPON YOUR FATHER'S DEATH, YOU RELIED ON YOUR MOTHER, HAWISE OF NORMANDY, WHO FOUGHT AGAINST REVOLT...

[5] ALAN III OF BRITTANY WAS THE COUSIN OF DUKE ROBERT I OF NORMANDY, WILLIAM'S FATHER.

TUROLD, I APPOINT YOU AS WILLIAM'S GUARDIAN.

OSBERN, YOU SHALL BE SENESCHAL.

AS FOR YOU, MY COUSIN GILBERT DE BRIONNE, YOU SHALL BE MY SON'S TUTOR!

AROUND THE YEAR 1030, MY FATHER GRANTED GILBERT, COUNT OF BRIONNE, THE LANDS OF ORBEC AND ITS THREE CASTELLANIES, LE SAP, BIENFAITE AND ORBEC.

I APPOINTED YOU COUNT OF EU! AND YOU TOOK ON THE RESPONSIBILITY OF DEFENDING THE DUCHY'S FRONTIERS!

ONE OF YOUR KNIGHTS, HERLUIN, HAS MADE AN OATH TO HAVE AN ABBEY BUILT.

AND THE PIOUS MAN FOUNDED HIS ABBEY IN THE BEC VALLEY LAST YEAR...

ENDOWING THE ABBEY WITH HIS OWN PERSONAL LAND.

BY ASKING ME TO APPROVE THIS CREATION, YOU HAVE BROUGHT THE PATRONAGE AND THE TITHE OF THE CHURCH OF ORBEC. I THANK YOU, GILBERT!

UNFORTUNATELY, MY FATHER'S PRUDENCE WAS TO PROVE JUSTIFIED. FOR SOON...

I AM BUT A MODEST PILGRIM FROM PIROU, IN COTENTIN. BUT I COME WITH NEWS...

HOW CAN I BEGIN...?

SPEAK!

FROM THEN ON, MY CHILDHOOD IN FALAISE WAS PARADISE LOST. NEVER AGAIN WOULD I SEE MY FATHER, HE WHO HAD BROUGHT ME UP NOBLY...

FROM THEN ON, WITHOUT HIM, I WAS ALONE.

IT WAS ON THE 2ND OF JULY 1035, IN NICAEA, IN BITHYNIA, ON HIS RETURN FROM HIS PILGRIMAGE THAT, SUDDENLY, YOUR FATHER...

...DIED!

SUCH IS MY NEWS

I AM SO SORRY. HE WAS AN ADMIRABLE PILGRIM.

VALIANT ROBERT, MY FATHER, WAS AGED TWENTY-FIVE.

SO ALONE.

THE DEATH OF A DUKE

Hence, at the age of 8, I inherited the title of Duke of Normandy and Count of Rouen. Yet, as soon as the news of my father's death spread, late 1035, everyone began to fear the imminence of fratricidal combat, to such an extent that the King of France Henry I, who as my suzerain should - on the contrary - have protected me, raised an army and tried to reclaim former French territories that had been lost via the Treaty of Saint-Clair-sur-Epte. This treaty, concluded in 911 between the Kingdom of France and my Viking ancestor Rollo, granted the latter with the territories that stretched between the River Epte and the sea in exchange for peace.

Hence, the French army entered my duchy. Around 1040, my fiefs fell into the hands of France, a kingdom perfectly in command of the situation in Normandy, Vexin in particular. Then Henry I himself encouraged the mayhem that reigned throughout my duchy where, freed from the rather tight stranglehold of my elders, the territory's leading families ambitiously entered the conflict in quest of revenge. Castles were built or fortified throughout my Normandy that now bathed in blood and fire. During these seven years of anarchy, famine and epidemics were rife.

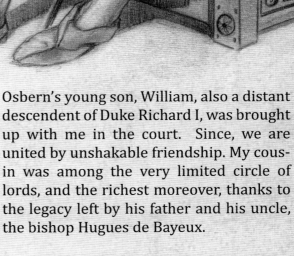

The Norman barons who had acknowledged my succession proved to be disloyal. Among them, the Richardides, descendents of the old dukes, just like me. Several of my greedy cousins tried the unthinkable: to assassinate my closest companions! More than ever, I was in danger... The eighty year-old lord of Harcourt, Turquetil, had been assassinated as early as 1036.

One episode in Vaudreuil particularly affected me. In 1040, as my faithful Seneschal Osbern de Crépon slept in my bedroom, a stranger entered. Poor Osbern! His throat was cut before my very eyes! Osbern, a rich nobleman, was already Seneschal under my father's reign. I will always remember his sacrifice.

Osbern's young son, William, also a distant descendent of Duke Richard I, was brought up with me in the court. Since, we are united by unshakable friendship. My cousin was among the very limited circle of lords, and the richest moreover, thanks to the legacy left by his father and his uncle, the bishop Hugues de Bayeux.

Osbern's murderer was soon to be unmasked. He was William, son of Roger de Montgommery whose family had always refused to acknowledge my legitimacy. Vengeful, the provost Barnon in turn assassinated Osbern's murderer. Later, when the time came, I remembered... and rewarded his descendants.

One of Barnon's sons took part in the future conquest as William FitzOsbern's dapifer.

When he was told of Osbern's murder, the regent Alan of Brittany gave the defence of my rights as a pretext to examine the castral mound in Saint-Germain, located between Livarot and Argentan and home to the Montgommery family. In September, Alan besieged the mound but, as he was about to capture it, he fell victim to a seizure. He was taken to Vimoutier where he died on the 1st of October 1040. Had he been poisoned? He was 43. The expedition led by the man who personally claimed my duchy had failed. As Richard I's grandson, he was buried alongside the first dukes in the Abbey Church of the Holy Trinity in Fécamp.

Following this murder, the powerful Count of Eu, Gilbert de Brionne, was appointed by the regency council as my tutor. This Richardide, who was fighting with the Giroie family over the Pays d'Ouche, attacked their fief in Montreuil-l'Argillé. The Giroies asked to negotiate with Gilbert. He accepted. But as he came down from his horse, two of the Giroies' men stabbed him.

The plot to murder Gilbert de Brionne had been hatched by Ralph de Gacé, AKA "Donkey Head", one of the Archbishop Robert II's sons. Jealous of Gilbert's influence on me, Ralph accused Robert de Vitot, guardian of Gilbert's sons, of being involved in the tragedy; Vitot immediately sought refuge with Baldwin of Flanders. Without daring to dethrone me, my new tutor became constable of Normandy in 1041. Gilbert's three sons were sent into exile and their fiefs were incorporated within my estate.

The Turold brothers, both guardians and lords from Pont-Audemer, were also assassinated in 1042. All of these conspiracies that had struck my close circle - I lost three of my protectors by assassination - appeared to be the doings of the famous Richardides, my cousins...

[6] Ost: feudal army.

After all these murders, a faction of barons was in a position to claim the duchy for my cousin Nicolas, a monk in Fécamp. The solution to push him aside consisted in placing him in charge of an abbey, despite his young age of 15! And a unique opportunity arose, in the form of the restored Abbey of St. Ouen in Rouen. There, so close to me, he could no longer makes plots behind my back. Hence, in 1042, Nicolas became the Abbot of St. Ouen...

It was in Falaise, in 1042, that I received my baptism of fire. Refusing my authority and that of my tutor, the Viscount of Exmes shut himself up inside his city walls. "What? Goz is refusing to obey the duke? He is but the guardian of the city, and I am William's tutor! We must raise the ost[6] and recapture the town!", Ralph exclaimed, adding in my direction, "You'll come with me! You're 14 now, you have reached the age to join our military action!" And our army besieged the fortress. Taking advantage of the dark of night, Goz furtively escaped. This one-day siege was my first experience as an armed horseman with sword and shield, an experience that marked the end of my childhood.

I then disappeared for many years. Had I sought refuge with my mother Herleva and my attentive stepfather Herluin, in Conteville? Had I gone into hiding in the place where my mother had stayed after her marriage, at the confluence of the Rivers Seine and Risle? Let me keep that secret for myself...

I was soon to oust Ralph from power without for as much confiscating his land, where he retreated till his death in 1051. Upon the death of his only son, I annexed his fiefs and those of his uncle Richard to re-incorporate these former territories within the ducal estate. Yes, I know, I have always been determined in revenge.

THE SCARS OF ILLEGITIMACY

ONE NIGHT

AN EXHAUSTED HORSEMAN

ALL I COULD HEAR WAS THE DULL SOUND OF MY HORSE'S SHOES AS THEY HAMMERED ACROSS THE FIELDS OF COTENTIN.

OUT OF BREATH, I RODE THE HEAVY CHARGING HORSE THROUGH THE BITTER NIGHT. A FANTASTIC NOCTURNAL CAVALCADE, OVER FORDS AND RIVERS, FORESTS AND FIELDS.

I HAD NARROWLY ESCAPED AN AMBUSH AT THE DUCAL MANOR IN VALOGNES.

THIS YOUNG HORSEMAN WAS ME, MYSELF, WILLIAM.

A PLOT OF WHICH I WAS THE TARGET, A MURDER ATTEMPT, A CRIME AGAINST THE DUKE... NEVER COULD I HAVE BELIEVED SUCH A THING POSSIBLE!

I WAS BUT AN EIGHTEEN YEAR-OLD TEENAGER. I WAS FLEEING THE VALOGNES COUNTRYSIDE WHERE, THE PREVIOUS DAY, I HAD GONE HUNTING. I FLED RELENTLESSLY EASTWARDS, WITH DEATH AT MY HEELS.

YES, THE BASTARD! HAVE YOU SEEN HIM?

WHICH ROAD DID HE TAKE?

HUBERT TOOK THEM TO A ROAD. THE WRONG ONE, OF COURSE.

THAT WAY! BUT WAIT, I'LL TAKE YOU THERE MYSELF! I'D LIKE TO STRIKE THE FIRST BLOW!

DISAPPEARED

EVAPORATED!

HOW CUNNING TO AVOID THE BUSY COUDRAY FORD!

THIS FORD IN THE PARISH TOWN OF OUFFIÈRES IS SURELY SAFER...

THEN, AVOIDING THE IMMENSE CINGLAIS FOREST TO THE NORTH...

AND THE NEARBY FIEF OF THE PERFIDIOUS RALPH DE TESSON, TO THE SOUTH...

WE RODE THROUGH LE CINGLAIS.

THE KEEP!

FALAISE, AT LAST!

THE CAPITAL OF THE DUCHY OF NORMANDY APPEARED AHEAD OF US...

...THE CITY OF MY MATERNAL UNCLE GAULTIER, MY CHILDHOOD BODYGUARD TO WHOM I OWED MY LIFE.

THE TRAITORS! THEIR MANHUNT HAS FAILED!

I HAVE SAVED MY SKIN THANKS TO YOUR FATHER, HUBERT'S LOYALTY.

BUT HAVE I ALSO SAVED MY DUCHY?

FROM FALAISE, I RESUMED THE BITTER STRUGGLE, THE OUTCOME OF WHICH WAS DECIDED IN BATTLE...

VAL-ÈS-DUNES, THE BARONS' SUBMISSION

Although, in Falaise, I was out of the reach of my pursuers, I preferred to take a cautious stance. My frantic flight was soon to take me to Rouen, from where I led an attack against the rebels, who, after my defeat in Valognes, had raised a vast army.

As vassal of Henry I, the King of France, I left my duchy in 1046 and headed for the royal residence in Poissy to ask for mutual support from my suzerain, despite the fact that he had paid little attention to my safety over my younger years. I said to him, "In 1031, upon the death of your father, Robert the Pious, my father helped you, Henry, King of France, to fight against the rebellious vassals spurred by your younger brother, Robert of Burgundy! And at the age of just 20, he was a vicious rival, supported by your cruel mother who had vainly tried to have you assassinated so that her favourite son would reign! You sought refuge by my father, and you were granted help and military support from his uncle Mauger, Count of Corbeil. Your defeated brother then proposed a truce. Since, you have reigned in peace. You gratefully granted the Norman people the suzerainty of the Vexin county. Today, threatened by my own vassals, I need your help!"

Hence, with help from my suzerain, I set off on campaign against my rebels. On the 10th of August 1047, I waged battle against thousands of men from the Norman barons' army at Val-ès-Dunes, in the Caen plain.

"Hey, remember the Baron of Creully!", Hamon le Dentu yelled to the French sovereign, who fell with his horse. "Saint-Amand!" Hamon cried as he thrust forward towards the fallen king, while Henry's vassals brought him another horse. Soon, a vengeful cry could be heard from the French camp: the baron, surrounded by several horsemen, was being attacked with swords and axes. He valiantly resisted, wounding many of his assailants before being struck himself, then falling to the ground and passing away.

Henry of France made a lucky escape: a spear fired by Néel from the Cotentin camp nearly slew him[8].

Fleeing the battlefield along with many other insurgents, Néel was caught up by my horsemen and was forced into exile in Brittany. From now on, the powers of his viscountcy in Cotentin were granted to a different lord. A lenient punishment compared to many other fleeing rebels who drowned in the Athis ford.

Only one traitor, Grimoald du Plessis, was imprisoned in Rouen. His castle was demolished and his estate confiscated for the profit of the Bayeux bishops.

Resourceful, Ralph de Tesson left the insurgent ranks before the start of the battle. And if he hit me as he had solemnly promised to do so before his fellow conspirators, it was but theatrically, by tapping me with his glove... before bowing down and joining my ranks along with his men!

[8] An 11th century poet wrote the following line: "From Cotentin came forth the lance, that once unhorsed the King of France."

The Battle of Val-ès-Dunes, what a watershed! The first in my reign! The victory over this coalition appeared to be decisive for my rise. My authority had been asserted and I resumed control over my duchy. Solid control. Behind the face of the young bastard, there now was a proud duke whose childhood troubles were behind him.

As I did with other rebels, I pardoned Néel and called him back to Normandy in 1054. My saviour, Hubert de Ryes, became my adviser and my gratitude transformed the family destiny of this country squire. His three sons became my faithful companions and, after our victory at Hastings, they were granted land in England.

This victory at Val-ès-Dunes needed to be utilised to win time in order to better counter the Richardides' hostility. In October 1047, a provincial council, reuniting bishops, abbots, clerics and knights on the hill at Vaucelles, a suburb of Caen, imposed a truce and the peace of God, in line with the movement to gradually prohibit private wars.

The truce of God, proclaimed by myself and the Norman bishops, was a second victory over the spirits. A godsend for me after my resounding victory over my vassals. From now on, in Normandy, wars between lords were to cease from Wednesday evening to Monday morning and during the harvest and major religious celebrations, on pain of exile.
A church, Sainte-Paix, was intended to remind the people of Caen of this important initiative. I am told that, in the 20th century, Caen has become famous for its "Memorial for Peace". It is but the continuation of the pacifistic vocation that I initiated in 1047!

Taking advantage of this lull, I gathered together a network of loyal and trustworthy men to support me in my governance of the duchy, appointing some of them to important positions, such as William FitzOsbern who became Seneschal, just like his father.

Via the distribution of strategic fiefs, I secured firmer control of my administrators, the viscounts. To the west of my duchy, I placed my two young half-brothers - my mother and the Viscount of Conteville's sons. To Odo, the elder of the two, I offered the lucrative bishopric of Bayeux in 1049. Around 1060, I granted Robert, his younger brother, the County of Mortain, on the border with the Duchy of Brittany. My half-sister Muriel married Odo, Viscount of Cotentin, who became one of my advisers in 1066.

Along with my uterine brothers, pillars of my power, a close circle of loyal men assisted me. Although the Montgommery family had been disloyal during my childhood, the powerful lord Roger de Montgommery became one of my friends and married Mabile, heiress to cruel William Talvas, in order to bring the rebellious seigniory of Bellême back into Norman hands. I named Roger Viscount of Hiémois, a position that had formerly been occupied by his father, who had since been banished from Normandy by the ducal power.

Pacifying conflicts between the pettifogging barons Giroie and Tosny, William FitzOsbern kept watch over the ducal castle in Bréteil, an indispensible strongpoint to the south, to counter any attacks by the King of France.

I entrusted the Château d'Ivry to a Richardide, the rich and valiant lord Roger de Beaumont, my most faithful companion and a man of precious support on the borders with the Pays d'Ouche.

Around 1050, I had the Château d'Acquigny built to control river trade on the Eure, which consisted mainly of Normandy's fishing, essential for Lent and for Fridays.

But I had other, vaster and far more exciting projects...

MATILDA OF LOVE AND OF FLANDERS

I WAS 23. SINCE VAL-ÈS-DUNES, MY AUTHORITY OVER MY VASSALS HAD BEEN FIRMLY ESTABLISHED.

BEAUTIFUL AND GENEROUS MATILDA OF FLANDERS, DAUGHTER OF BALDWIN OF LILLE, COUNT OF FLANDERS...

CONTRACTING A NOBLE-BLOODED MARRIAGE WOULD HELP ME TO EXTEND IT BEYOND THE LIMITS OF MY DUCHY.

AND OF ADELA OF FRANCE, COUNTESS OF CORBIE... THE PERFECT CHOICE.

ON HER MOTHER'S SIDE, MATILDA WAS HENRY I, THE KING OF FRANCE'S NIECE. BY THIS POLITICAL UNION IMPOSED UPON MY BRIDE, I COULD FURTHER DEVELOP MY LOYAL NETWORK...

YET, WHEN THE COUNT TOLD HIS DAUGHTER OF MY PROPOSAL, SHE REFUSED...

OUT OF THE QUESTION!

AS LEGEND HAS IT, INFURIATED, I RODE AT GREAT SPEED TOWARDS FLANDERS.

WHEN I ARRIVED, I FLUNG MATILDA TO THE GROUND AND TORE OPEN HER DRESS WITH MY SPURS.

STRANGELY, THE YOUNG WOMAN APPEARED CAPTIVATED BY MY ATTITUDE...

I WANT NO OTHER SPOUSE THAN YOU! YOU HAVE JUST PROVEN YOUR DETERMINATION!

WHAT AN AGREEABLE LEGEND!

FROM NOW ON, NOTHING COULD STOP OUR LONG-AWAITED UNION, WHICH WAS RECOMMENDED BY THE NORMANDY BARONY. NOTHING, EXCEPT THE POPE. POPE LEO IX HAD ORGANISED A COUNCIL IN REIMS ON THE 3RD OF AUGUST 1049, TO ASSERT, AMONG OTHER MOTIVES, HIS WILL TO PROHIBIT "INCESTUOUS" MARRIAGES.

I FORBID BALDWIN V OF FLANDERS TO GIVE HIS DAUGHTER'S HAND TO WILLIAM OF NORMANDY, AND I FORBID THAT THE DUKE OF NORMANDY ACCEPT HER AS HIS SPOUSE!

TO JUSTIFY THIS INTERDICTION, HE INVOKES HIS CONDEMNATION OF INCESTUOUS UNIONS!

BECAUSE OF CONSANGUINITY? SINCE MY DAUGHTER MATILDA IS YOUR COUSIN, THIS UNION WOULD BE "INCESTUOUS"...

IN APRIL, POPE LEO IX HAD HELD A COUNCIL IN ROME CONDEMNING SIMONY, THE PURCHASE OR SALE OF ECCLESIASTICAL PRACTICES, AND NICOLAISM, PRIESTS INDULGING IN MARITAL RELATIONS.

HE HAD DECIDED TO TRAVEL ACROSS CHRISTIAN EUROPE TO ENERGETICALLY DEFEND HIS REFORM.

BUT OUR KINSHIP IS DISTANT, FIVE GENERATIONS OFF...

MAY THIS POPE FEAR US! HE FEARS THE UNION OF OUR TWO GREAT POWERS, FLEMISH AND NORMAN...[9]

I GRANT YOU MY DAUGHTER'S HAND, WILLIAM. FOR I SEE TWO AMOROUS LOVEBIRDS.

CLAC!!

OUR MARRIAGE WAS CELEBRATED IN 1050. AND ALTHOUGH IT WAS A PRINCELY WEDDING, IT WAS A DISCREET ONE.

HERLEVA AND HER HUSBAND HERLUIN ARE PRESENT... BUT BALDWIN IS ABSENT, ISN'T HE?

WILLIAM IS AS TALL AS HIS MATILDA IS SMALL!

SHE IS SAID TO MEASURE 1.5 METRES, AND WILLIAM 1.75 METRES!

FROM OUR UNION, AT LEAST NINE CHILDREN WERE BORN, 4 OF THEM SONS: ROBERT CURTHOSE, BORN CIRCA 1051, CECILIA, ADELIZA AND RICHARD, WILLIAM RUFUS, CONSTANCE, MATILDA, ADELA OF ENGLAND AND HENRY BEAUCLERC, BORN LATE 1068.

WE THEN HEADED FOR ROUEN TO CONTINUE THE FESTIVITIES AND HONOURS IN THE CAPITAL OF THE DUCHY.

PROOF OF A HAPPY MARRIAGE, I AM THE ONLY DUKE TO HAVE HAD NEITHER MISTRESS, NOR BASTARD.

I SENT LANFRANC DE PAVIE, THE BEC-HELLOUIN ABBOT, TO ROME TO PLEAD OUR CAUSE.

[9] POPE LEO IX ALSO HATED WILLIAM'S NORMAN COUSINS, WHO WERE CONQUERING SOUTHERN ITALY.

AFTER 1050, I WAS STRICKEN BY TRAGEDY: MY MOTHER'S DEATH.

HERLEVA WAS BURIED IN THE ABBEY OF GRESTAIN, NEAR CONTEVILLE, WHICH SHE HAD FOUNDED WITH HER HUSBAND IN 1050, AFTER THE LATTER HAD BEEN HEALED OF A SKIN DISEASE.

FOLLOWING MY STEPFATHER'S ADVICE, I AUTHORISED GILBERT DE BRIONNE'S SONS, AND ESPECIALLY THEIR GUARDIAN, WHO HAD FOR A LONG TIME BEEN WRONGLY ACCUSED OF BEING BEHIND THE DEATH OF HIS OWN TUTOR, TO RETURN TO NORMANDY.

GEOFFREY MARTEL, COUNT OF ANJOU, HAD PREVIOUSLY CONQUERED DOMFRONT AND ALENÇON. AT THE TIME, WE WERE RIVALS. THE KING OF FRANCE SUPPORTED THEM IN TURNS IN ORDER TO CONTAIN OUR POWER.

SINCE THEN, IN THE SPRING OF 1049, I HAD INVADED MAINE. THEN IN 1051, WHEN THE KING OF FRANCE WAS THREATENING MARTEL'S REAR TERRITORIES, I BESIEGED DOMFRONT.

THE SKIN, THE TANNER'S SKIN! THE SKIN, THE TANNER'S SKIN![10]

HOW DARE THEY REMIND ME OF MY GRANDFATHER'S TRADE, OF MY ILLEGITIMACY!!

THEY WILL PAY FOR IT!!

INFURIATED, I ATTACKED THE CITY.

PENDING HIS SURRENDER, I HEADED FOR ALENÇON. I HAD DECIDED TO TAKE THE TOWN BY SURPRISE!

HAVE THE HANDS AND FEET OF 32 PRISONERS CHOPPED OFF! THEN CATAPULT THEM INSIDE THE FORTRESS!

ALENÇON CAPITULATED BEFORE SUCH CRUELTY.

AS DID DOMFRONT, IN 1052. THE GARRISON SURRENDERED IN EXCHANGE FOR PROMISED MERCY. THE DUCHY'S SOUTHERN BORDER HAD BEEN PERMANENTLY BROADENED...

[10] INSULTING ALLUSION TO WILLIAM'S MATERNAL GRANDFATHER'S TRADE.

— 21 —

AS IS MY MARRIAGE, THIS MILITARY SUCCESS IS A WORRY TO THE KING OF FRANCE. IT IS OVERTHROWING HIS ALLIANCE IN THE CONFLICT BETWEEN MAINE AND NORMANDY...

HENRY IS ALSO TAKING SIDES WITH THE REBELLIOUS NORMAN BARONS!

I AM TOO POWERFUL A VASSAL. HE NOW FEELS THE NECESSITY TO LIMIT MY EXPANSION!

HE PERMANENTLY MADE PEACE WITH MARTEL IN AUGUST 1052.

THEIR ALLEGIANCE IS CONTINUALLY STRENGTH-ENING...

WARY OF MY UNCLE WILLIAM, WHO HAD BUILT THE CHÂTEAU D'ARQUES, I HAD A DUCAL GARRISON ESTABLISHED THERE.

DURING MY CHILDHOOD, WILLIAM OF TALOU, DUKE RICHARD II AND PAPIA'S SON, HAD ADMINISTERED THE DUCHY. AROUND 1037, HE HAD BEEN GRANTED THE COUNTIES OF TALOU AND ARQUES.[11]

SHORTLY AFTER HIS ESTABLISHMENT THERE, DEFENDERS OPENED THE FORTRESS TO WILLIAM OF TALOU THE COUNT PREPARED AN UPRISING THERE, IN REPROACH OF MY ILLEGITIMACY!

AND IN THE MIDST OF THE YEAR 1053...

A REBELLION WAS RAISED IN ARQUES, I RUSHED THERE IN THE AUTUMN. THEN I ENTRUSTED MY FAITHFUL COMPANION GAUTIER I GIFFARD WITH THE TASK OF CONTINUING THE SIEGE, COUNTING ON HUNGER...

THIS REVOLT WAS ALL THE MORE WORRYING FOR ME SINCE WILLIAM OF TALOU HAD BEEN GRANTED MILITARY SUPPORT FROM THE KING OF FRANCE AND FROM ENGUERRAND II, THE COUNT OF PONTHIEU.

MY HALF-SISTER ADELAIDE HAD MARRIED ENGUERRAND.

BUT HENRY AND ENGUERRAND'S OST HAD FAILED TO FREE THE CASTLE.

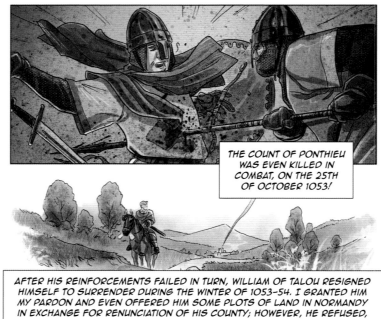

THE COUNT OF PONTHIEU WAS EVEN KILLED IN COMBAT, ON THE 25TH OF OCTOBER 1053!

THE COUNTY OF ARQUES/TALOU THEN DISAPPEARED.

CONSEQUENTLY, I CONFISCATED THE FIEF OF AUMALE, UPGRADED IT TO THE STATUS OF COUNTY AND OFFERED IT TO ADELAIDE, ENGUERRAND'S WIDOW.

AFTER HIS REINFORCEMENTS FAILED IN TURN, WILLIAM OF TALOU RESIGNED HIMSELF TO SURRENDER DURING THE WINTER OF 1053-54. I GRANTED HIM MY PARDON AND EVEN OFFERED HIM SOME PLOTS OF LAND IN NORMANDY IN EXCHANGE FOR RENUNCIATION OF HIS COUNTY; HOWEVER, HE REFUSED, PREFERRING EXILE BY EUSTACHE, THE COUNT OF BOULOGNE.

[11] COUNTY LOCATED TO THE NORTHEAST OF NORMANDY ON THE BORDER WITH PICARDY.

SHORTLY AFTER HIS BROTHER WILLIAM OF TALOU WAS BANISHED, UNDESERVING MAUGER WAS DEPOSED OF HIS POSITION AS ARCHBISHOP OF ROUEN AT THE COUNCIL OF LISIEUX, IN MAY 1055.

AS CHIEF OF THE OPPONENTS TO CHURCH REFORM, HE CAN BUT ABANDON THIS METROPOLITAN SEAT!

BRAVE MAURILLE, A FORMER MONK FROM FÉCAMP, REPLACED HIM UPON MY REQUEST.

ASSERTING MY POWER AND ELIMINATING THE RICHARDIDES, I EMBARKED ON REFORMING THE NORMAN CHURCH, OPPOSED TO ANY PRIESTS WHO TOOK CONCUBINES.

MAUGER, WHO WAS CONSTANTLY ACCUSED OF REBELLING AGAINST MY POWER, WAS SENTENCED TO BANISHMENT THEN SENT TO GUERNSEY.

WHERE HE DROWNED ...

IN CONTRAST, I WELCOMED THE NORMAN ABBOT ROBERT OF JUMIÈGES IN 1052, WHEN THE ARCHBISHOP OF CANTERBURY, A LOYAL FRIEND OF KING EDWARD, WAS FORCED TO HASTILY LEAVE ENGLAND.

THIS DEPARTURE HAS BEEN IMPOSED ON ALL NORMANS BY MEANS OF A SENTENCE PASSED BY THE ENGLISH HIGH ASSEMBLY ON THE 14TH OF SEPTEMBER. ROBERT SOUGHT REFUGE IN JUMIÈGES, DEPOSED OF HIS ARCHBISHOPRIC.

COULD THIS DEPARTURE BE SUBSEQUENT TO EARL GODWIN OF WESSEX'S RETURN TO ENGLAND?

YES! HE IS THE SPEARHEAD OF THE ANGLO-DANISH PARTY. NOTORIOUS HAROLD'S FATHER!!

THE PREVIOUS YEAR, KING EDWARD HAD ENTRUSTED ROBERT OF JUMIÈGES WITH THE MISSION OF COMING TO NORMANDY TO BRING ME NEWS OF CAPITAL IMPORTANCE... ...A PROMISE I SHALL NOT FORGET WHEN THE TIME COMES.

HEIRLESS, THE KING OF ENGLAND HAS CHOSEN YOU TO BE HIS SUCCESSOR...

ALREADY ...

WE WILL REUNITE THE TWO ARMIES BEFORE ROUEN. HENCE OBLIGING WILLIAM TO DIVIDE HIS OST!

TO THE NORTH, THE ARMY LED BY ODO, BROTHER OF KING HENRY I, REACHED THE PAYS DE BRAY. TO THE SOUTH, THE ARMY LED BY THE KING OF FRANCE AND THE COUNT OF ANJOU ATTACKED THE COUNTY OF EVREUX.

SOON, AT THE END OF THE WINTER OF 1053, TWO FRANCO-ANGEVIN ARMIES INVADED THE DUCHY.

TO DEFEND MY INTERESTS, I RAISED TWO ARMIES, ONE LED BY MYSELF AGAINST THE KING'S ARMY AND THE OTHER COMMANDED BY GAUTIER GIFFARD AND ROBERT D'EU IN THE PAYS DE BRAY.

THE FRENCH TROOPS SPENT THE NIGHT IN MORTEMER SUR EALNE.

TAKING ADVANTAGE OF THEIR NEGLIGENCE, THE SECOND NORMAN ARMY ATTACKED THE KING'S BROTHER'S CAMP THERE, CUTTING THE DRUNKEN FRENCH INTO PIECES.

EASY VICTORY!

RAOUL II DE TOSNY WILL ANNOUNCE THE EVENT TO THE ENEMY OST!

AT THE TOP OF A HILL, THE DUCAL HERALD PROCLAIMED THE FRANCO-ANGEVIN ARMY'S DEFEAT.

UPON THIS ANNOUNCEMENT, THE KING OF FRANCE AND THE COUNT OF ANJOU SOUNDED THE RETREAT.

ROGER DE MORTIMER LOST ALL HIS FIEFS; I TOOK THEM FROM HIM IN RETALIATION AND IMMEDIATELY BANISHED HIM FOR HAVING FREED THE PRISONER RAOUL IV DE VEXIN, IMPRISONED AFTER THE BATTLE.

RAOUL SOUGHT REFUGE AT THE COURT OF VALOIS FROM WHERE HE CONTINUED TO FIGHT ON THE FRENCH SIDE.

AFTER 1055, IN REWARD FOR HIS FAVOURS, I CONCEDED THE FIEF OF LONGUEVILLE TO MY FAITHFUL COMPANION GIFFARD.

A VASSAL, FREE AND JUBILANT IN CONQUEST...

Bellicose, Henry of France came back to Normandy in 1057, allied more than ever with the Angevin Count Geoffrey Martel. So I challenged the Count of Anjou, requesting that he quickly travel to Ambrières, on the border with Maine. The alliance against me had been reformed, and the Franco-Angevin troops raised in Brittany and Touraine surrounded me in this castle, standing on a rocky spur. But I eventually forced my assailants to lift the siege, before retreating to Falaise.

This reverse of fortune enraged the King of France! His troops secretly advanced northwards towards Bessin. From the bastion of Saint-Pierre on the River Dives, his army pillaged the Bessin area without challenging us. We had cunningly fled. At a few hundred against a few thousand, I preferred to dodge, hiding in the forest of Bavent, waiting for my hour to come. Since the wood ran alongside the only possible route for the French troops, my hour indeed came. On the 22nd of March, the French army marched up the Orne, crossed the river at the Bénouville ford and headed eastwards. I could see Henry I leading his ost. I advised, "Let them go past, they are heading for the Dives. They will cross it via the Varaville causeway, and the tide is rising..." The Dives bay occupied an immense stretch of salted land covered with shallow water at low tide, but that needed to be crossed in order to reach Rouen, the capital of the duchy. The king and his vanguard crossed the impetuous coastal river over a wooden bridge and reached the opposite bank, followed by their rearguard. We then resounded the signal, "Attack!" Not far from the bridge, the king's rearguard saw my troops thrusting upon them. Many perished under sword. Surrounded by the marshes to the south and the sea to the north, they had no other choice but to go back to the bridge, which collapsed under their weight, as the alarmed army rabble either drowned or was taken prisoner. From a hilltop, the Count of Anjou and the king watched their demise. History was repeating itself. Just like in the year 945, a Norman duke had defeated

a King of France here. I pushed my advantage as far as Dreux and imposed peace upon the king who never again set foot on my duchy, henceforth respected. Varaville was to seal my continental power.

From now on, I could look after internal affairs. The Count of Mortain, who was banished and forced into exile in southern Italy, was immediately replaced by my half-brother Robert. Around 1058, Maud de Montgommery, heiress to Bellême, married Robert. This union was to permanently seal loyalty from the turbulent house of Bellême, all the more so thanks to the rapid progeny offered by Maud and my half-brother.

So I set to building. When the King of France crossed my duchy in 1057, I had regretted that the town of Caen, so close to both Bessin and Cotentin, was not a stronghold. The duchy needed to be consolidated from the west; Caen was to become its capital and a castle was to be built on an outcrop.

I also needed to look after sorting out the question of my marriage with the new Pope Nicholas II. Now an ally of the Norman counts in Italy, in order to counter the emperor's influence over Rome, he acknowledged our union provided that each of us build an abbey in Caen. What an opportune proposal: Caen was my favourite city, far more strategic than Rouen and close to the sea, and in a better position to control western Normandy, which remained somewhat defiant of the Rouen dukes. And I, a pious man, was of builders' blood. Matilda immediately founded the Ladies Abbey in Caen, devoted to the Holy Trinity. Reserved for Benedictine monks, the abbey-church of the Men's Abbey was also erected in 1063, and devoted to St. Stephen. Hence, Matilda and I were absolved. I chose one of them for my sepulchre and the other for that of my beloved wife.

Thankfully, the future appeared brighter for my duchy. In 1060, the death of my leading enemies, the Count of Anjou in November and the Frankish King in August, facilitated my advancement. The previous year, permanent peace had been signed between Henry I and myself, including the possible liberation of the Varaville prisoners. Since Philip, the heir to the throne, was but 8 years old, the regency of France was entrusted to his uncle. Who was no other than Baldwin of Flanders, my own father-in-law! Hence, peace was established between France and Normandy.

From now on, I was free to conquer Maine, a region located between Anjou and Normandy. The death of the Count Herbert du Maine in 1062 spurred an ambitious feudal lord, Gautier de Gouy, to claim his county. Yet, Herbert, who had no heirs, had already bequeathed it to me upon his death.

The Count of Maine, who had escaped from occupied Le Mans to seek refuge at my court in 1056, had thus paid me homage. The lords of Maine refused to grant me my legacy and chose Gautier as their count. I therefore set off to conquer Maine, taking its fortresses one by one, then Le Mans, hence guaranteeing the protection of the south of my duchy. To consolidate these ramparts, Herbert's sister, Marguerite du Maine, was engaged to my son Robert.

So I captured Gautier and his wife, who both died in custody in Falaise in 1063, in uncertain circumstances... Certain venomous tongues speak of poisoning, I know... They had no children... Gautier's death suited me fine: he was the last surviving child of Goda, King Edward the Confessor's sister. As such, he could well have, one day, claimed the throne of England upon Edwards's death...

During this period, my Normandy gained greater importance over the Capetians, to such an extent that sixty year-old Raoul du Vexin, a French vassal, preferred me to the King of France as his ally.

The situation very quickly became complicated in Maine. Since the death of my daughter-in-law Marguerite in 1063, the county passed to my son Robert... On paper, but not out in the field. To quell the massive nobiliary rebellion, I adopted the scorched earth strategy, having each and every insurgent castle burnt down, in Mayenne, then in Le Mans where I had my son's title of count acknowledged. Since he was still a child, I became the true master of Maine.

Without for as much forgetting Rouen. On the 1st of October 1063, the city's cathedral was consecrated by Maurille, in the presence of the Bishop of Avranches, Jean d'Ivry and myself. A little later, the relics of my ancestors Rollo and William Longsword were transferred to the top of the nave. As a vassal, I was free. A man of trust, for my memory served me well. Contrary to many others...

BETRAYAL!

AFTER A 24-YEAR REIGN OVER A KINGDOM THAT WAS ALLIED WITH NORMANDY, THE KING OF ENGLAND, EDWARD THE CONFESSOR, DIED ON THE 5TH OF JANUARY 1066.

WITH NEITHER CHILD NOR DIRECT HEIR TO THE THRONE. FOR ME, HIS COUSIN, THINGS WERE PERFECTLY CLEAR...

EARLIER, IN 1013, MY GRANDFATHER DUKE RICHARD II HAD WELCOMED EXILED MEMBERS OF HIS COURT: EDWARD, HIS YOUNGER BROTHER ALFRED AND THEIR FATHER, KING AETHELRED THE UNREADY.

ATTACKED BY VIKING RAIDS, HIS ENGLISH KINGDOM HAD FALLEN INTO THE HANDS OF THE DANISH KING CNUT.

IN 1018, THEY HAD A SON, HARTHACNUT.

EMMA, AETHELRED'S WIFE AND MY GREAT AUNT ON MY FATHER'S SIDE, STAYED IN ENGLAND AND MARRIED CNUT![12]

AS HIS DESIGNATED SUCCESSOR, HARTHACNUT BECAME KING UPON HIS FATHER'S DEATH IN NOVEMBER 1035. OR AT LEAST ON PAPER. HE WAS RETAINED IN DENMARK, AMIDST THE CONFUSION OF A DISINTEGRATING EMPIRE...

IN 1036, IN RESPONSE TO EMMA'S REQUEST TO SEE HER SONS AGAIN, EDWARD AND ALFRED BOARDED SHIPS AND HEADED FOR ENGLAND, IN COMMAND OF A CONSIDERABLE NORMAN ARMY, DETERMINED TO OBTAIN RECOGNITION OF THEIR RIGHT TO THE ENGLISH THRONE.

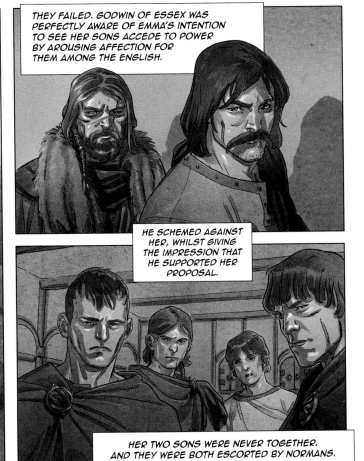

THEY FAILED. GODWIN OF ESSEX WAS PERFECTLY AWARE OF EMMA'S INTENTION TO SEE HER SONS ACCEDE TO POWER BY AROUSING AFFECTION FOR THEM AMONG THE ENGLISH.

HE SCHEMED AGAINST HER, WHILST GIVING THE IMPRESSION THAT HE SUPPORTED HER PROPOSAL.

HER TWO SONS WERE NEVER TOGETHER. AND THEY WERE BOTH ESCORTED BY NORMANS.

[12] IT WAS THANKS TO HIS KINSHIP THAT WILLIAM, HIS GREAT NEPHEW, WAS ABLE TO CLAIM THE ENGLISH THRONE IN 1066.

BETRAYED BY GODWIN, ALFRED WAS CAUGHT IN AN AMBUSH. HE WAS THEN LOCKED UP IN THE MONASTERY ON THE ISLE OF ELY WHERE HIS EYES WERE GOUGED OUT AND HE DIED IN FEBRUARY 1037.

UPON NEWS OF ALFRED'S ARREST, HIS MOTHER SECRETLY SENT EDWARD TO NORMANDY. ACCUSED OF TREACHERY BY GODWIN, SHE WAS SENT INTO EXILE WITH BALDWIN V.

EDWARD ONLY RETURNED TO HIS KINGDOM IN 1042, AFTER THE SUDDEN DEATH OF HIS HALF-BROTHER HARTHACNUT IN JUNE.

CROWNED KING OF ENGLAND IN THE EASTER OF 1043 IN WINCHESTER, EDWARD RESTORED THE ANGLO-SAXON ROYALTY, THE FIRST ENGLISH ROYAL HOUSE.

SO AS FAR AS I WAS CONCERNED, THINGS WERE PERFECTLY CLEAR! BUT NOT TO EVERYONE...

ONE NORWEGIAN IN PARTICULAR, HARALD HARDRADA, THE POWERFUL KING OF NORWAY,

TOGETHER WITH A POWERFUL ANGLO-SAXON ARISTOCRAT, HAROLD GODWINSON, EARL OF WESSEX AND THE DECEASED KING'S BROTHER-IN-LAW.[13]

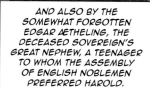

AND ALSO BY THE SOMEWHAT FORGOTTEN EDGAR ÆTHELING, THE DECEASED SOVEREIGN'S GREAT NEPHEW, A TEENAGER TO WHOM THE ASSEMBLY OF ENGLISH NOBLEMEN PREFERRED HAROLD.

SHORTLY BEFORE HIS DEATH, THE KING MAY HAVE CHANGED HIS MIND, DESIGNATING HAROLD AS HIS SUCCESSOR IN THE PRESENCE OF STIGAND, THE ARCHBISHOP OF CANTERBURY...

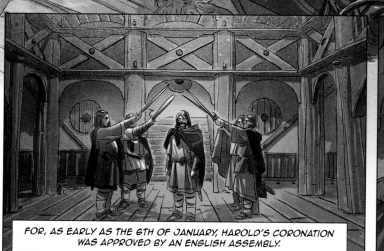

FOR, AS EARLY AS THE 6TH OF JANUARY, HAROLD'S CORONATION WAS APPROVED BY AN ENGLISH ASSEMBLY.

[13] EDWARD DIED ON THE 5TH OF JANUARY 1066.

I WANTED TO CONSULT YOU ON MY PROJECT TO LAUNCH AN EXPEDITION TO ENGLAND TO CLAIM MY RIGHTFUL INHERITANCE.

BUT WILLIAM!! ENGLAND IS BETTER ARMED!

DUKE ROBERT ALREADY GATHERED A FLEET IN FÉCAMP THIRTY YEARS AGO. A STORM SENT THEM ASTRAY, TO JERSEY! INSTEAD OF INVADING ENGLAND, YOUR FATHER PILLAGED BRITTANY!

COWARDS, YOU ARE COWARDS!

WILLIAM, FITZOSBERN IS RIGHT!!

I PROMISE TO PROVIDE 60 SHIPS TO CROSS THE ENGLISH CHANNEL, SO YOU, NORMAN BARONS, PROVIDE THE NECESSARY LOGISTICS FOR THIS EXPEDITION!

I KNOW HAROLD. WHEN HE CAME TO NORMANDY, HE TOOK PART IN THE CAMPAIGN I LED AGAINST DUKE CONAN IN BRITTANY, SAVING TWO SOLDIERS FROM THE RIVER COUESNON SINKING SANDS...

HIS BRAVERY WILL SEAL HIS DEMISE!

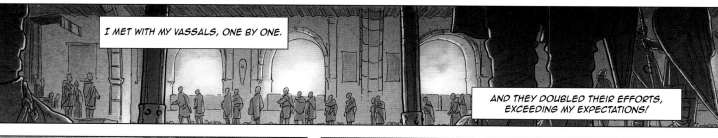

I MET WITH MY VASSALS, ONE BY ONE.

AND THEY DOUBLED THEIR EFFORTS, EXCEEDING MY EXPECTATIONS!

ROBERT DE MORTAIN?

I PROMISE TO CONTRIBUTE 120 SHIPS TO THE FLEET!

AND YOU, ODO?

I PROMISE YOU 100 SHIPS!

THEY BOTH ACCOMPANIED ON MY CONQU. THIS WAS NOT CASE OF ROG. DE BEAUMONT, NEVERTHELE CONTRIBUTE TOWARDS THE OF THE INVAS. BY FITTING SHIPS FOR TR TRANSPOR

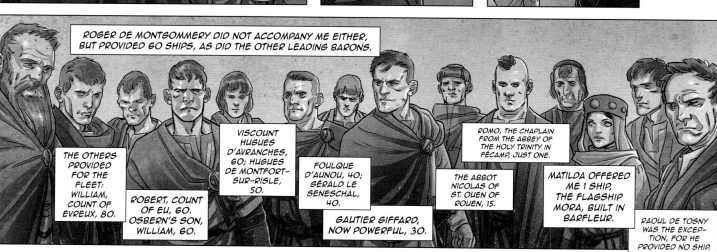

ROGER DE MONTGOMMERY DID NOT ACCOMPANY ME EITHER, BUT PROVIDED 60 SHIPS, AS DID THE OTHER LEADING BARONS.

THE OTHERS PROVIDED FOR THE FLEET: WILLIAM, COUNT OF EVREUX, 80.

ROBERT, COUNT OF EU, 60. OSBERN'S SON, WILLIAM, 60.

VISCOUNT HUGUES D'AVRANCHES, 60; HUGUES DE MONTFORT-SUR-RISLE, 50.

FOULQUE D'AUNOU, 40; GÉRALD LE SENESCHAL, 40.

GAUTIER GIFFARD, NOW POWERFUL, 30.

ROMO, THE CHAPLAIN FROM THE ABBEY OF THE HOLY TRINITY IN FÉCAMP, JUST ONE.

THE ABBOT NICOLAS OF ST. OUEN OF ROUEN, 15.

MATILDA OFFERED ME 1 SHIP, THE FLAGSHIP MORA, BUILT IN BARFLEUR.

RAOUL DE TOSNY WAS THE EXCEPTION, FOR HE PROVIDED NO SHIP.

ON THE OUTLOOK FOR ALLIES, I OBTAINED SUPPORT FROM THE POPE ALEXANDER II WHO HAD BEEN GIVEN INSTRUCTION AT THE ABBEY OF BEC, UNDER LANFRANC.

JEAN DE FÉCAMP HAD OBTAINED BENEDICTION FROM THE POPE, WHO EVEN HAD HIS OWN PONTIFICAL STANDARD SENT!

ALONG WITH SACRED RELICS. THE SUPREME PONTIFF HAS EVEN THREATENED ANY OBJECTORS WITH EXCOMMUNICATION, WILLIAM!

I MADE SURE THAT MY BRETON, FLEMISH AND ANGEVIN NEIGH-BOURS WOULD NOT SEIZE MY DUCHY DURING MY ABSENCE.

IN EIGHT MONTHS, THE NORMAN ARMY WAS READY.

MANY SOLDIERS WERE YOUNGER BROTHERS FOR WHOM THE RIGHT OF PRIMOGENITURE LEFT LITTLE HOPE OF INHERITING A FIEF.

I PROMISE THAT IF THEY JOIN ME WITH THEIR OWN HORSES, ARMOUR AND WEAPONS, I WILL REWARD THEM IN MY NEW KINGDOM!

IN THE VAST FOREST OF BUR-LE-ROY[14], IN BESSIN, THE OLD OAK TREES WERE FELLED AND SQUARED.

GREEN WOOD TOO, FAILING SUFFICIENT DRY WOOD, FOR THE SHIPS WOULD ONLY HAVE ONE RETURN JOURNEY TO MAKE!

INTENSE ACTIVITY OCCUPIED THE DIVES ESTUARY, A COMMERCIAL AND WHALE FISHING PORT.

ON THE RIVERSIDE, FLOATING LOGS SUPPLIED THE SHIPYARDS WHERE THE HUNDRED SHIPS PROMISED BY ODO WERE BUILT.

IN THE ORNE, DIVES AND EURE VALLEYS, LUMBERJACKS AND CARPENTERS SWEAT BLOOD TO TRANSFORM THE NORMAN OAK TRUNKS INTO THE SHIPS THAT WOULD COLLECTIVELY FORM AN INVASION FLEET OF AROUND 700 ESNEQUES. OTHERS WERE REQUISITIONED OR HIRED.

[14] NOW KNOWN AS THE CERISY-BALLEROY FOREST.

AN ARMY ESTIMATED AT 7,000 TO 8,000 MEN, 2,000 OF THEM HORSEMEN, WAS SOON TO AWAIT FAVOURABLE CONDITIONS.

IN VARAVILLE, HORSEMEN AND FOOT SOLDIERS ARE TRAINING IN EMBARKING AND LANDING MANOEUVRES!

A STRANGE PHENOMENON APPEARED IN THE NORMANDY SKY ON THE 24TH OF APRIL...

A COMET? AN OMINOUS SIGN FOR HAROLD?

I REUNITED MY LEADING VASSALS AT THE CHÂTEAU DE BONNEVILLE MID-JUNE.

I MUST ENSURE THE SAFETY OF MY DUCHY DURING MY ABSENCE.

HENCE, I ASK YOU TO SWEAR ALLEGIANCE TO MY ELDEST SON, ROBERT.

DURING MY CONQUEST, I ENTRUST THE DUCHY'S REGENCY TO MATILDA. ROGER DE BEAUMONT, LANFRANC AND ROGER DE MONTGOMMERY WILL BE HER ADVISERS.

SHORTLY BEFORE THE SUMMER SOLSTICE, ON THE 18TH OF JUNE, IN CAEN'S BOURG-L'ABESSE QUARTER, THE EASTERN PARTS OF THE LADIES ABBEY WERE CONSECRATED.

THE SAME DAY, CECILIA, MY ELDEST DAUGHTER, WAS OFFERED TO GOD: AT THE AGE OF FIVE, SHE ENTERED THE ABBEY'S BENEDICTINE COMMUNITY.

AS I HAD FOR MY BARONS, I ENDOWED THE HOLY TRINITY WITH LAND, FURNISHINGS AND INCOME.

IN 1060, FOLLOWING MATILDA'S WISHES, A COMMUNITY OF WOMEN TOOK UP RESIDENCE IN HER NEW FOUNDATION, A VAST PRIMITIVE CHURCH BUILT AROUND 1055. OVER AND ABOVE MY OWN FAMILY, I REUNITED THE ARCHBISHOP OF ROUEN, FOUR BISHOPS, EIGHT ABBOTS, TWO VISCOUNTS AND NINE BARONS IN THE CHURCH.

BY LATE JULY, EVERYTHING WAS

VALIANT HEARTS AND OVERTURNED STOMACHS

In July, the fleet and the ost were reunited in the gulf of the Dives, waiting for favourable winds.

On the morning of the 9th of September, the order to board resounded! At last! As I woke on the beach where I had slept under the moonlight, I could feel the oncoming western breeze! Failing south winds, that would take us to England, let's head east! We boarded that very evening and the fleet prepared to anchor at a point closer to England, Saint-Valéry in the Bay of Somme. From there, the English coast would be reached in just one night.

The crossing was gruelling for many soldiers who had never sailed before, and proved even tragic for certain ships that crashed against the cliffs. We anchored at Saint-Valéry. Hindered by northerly winds, my army waited patiently in the estuary for several days. With the exception of our rowing boats, the other square-rigged ships could only sail under rear winds... We had to wait for prevailing winds, and wait and wait... And the autumn equinox was near...

A wait that proved to be to my advantage, for I was soon informed of a second front in England[15]. The Yorkshire coast had been invaded by the Norwegian King Harald Hardrada's army. Hardrada was a pretender who, with help from Tostig, Harold's banished brother, had beaten Earl Edwin's English troops. Spies also informed me that Harold, far too confident, had left his fleet in the Thames...

In Saint-Valéry, the rain stopped on the night of the 27th to the 28th of September. And the wind came from the south! At dawn, I gave the long-awaited order. The armada set off, two hours after high tide. Its sails full with wind, it followed my flagship, the Mora. The Channel crossing was so quick that I ordered for us to anchor before dawn in the high seas, fearing we may meet with a hostile welcome by night.

A fire lit at the top of the Mora, together with the sound of a trumpet, were the combined signal to set off again. Straight towards the pole star!

Then, at dawn, I discovered the chalky cliffs of Sussex! My ship was faster, and waited for the others, its sails down and anchors dropped. The forest of masts soon appeared before us!
On the dawn of St. Michael's day, I approached Pevensey Bay. Archers and crossbowmen ran across the strand in hundreds. Incredible, not the slightest defence! Saint Michael, the patron saint of Normandy, was with us! The ebb of the tide left our fleet grounded on the shore. Then, valets and sailors unloaded the frisky horses and provisions. And the craftsmen discharged the three dismantled wooden castles before all the ships' masts were unstepped. And, early afternoon, under the enthusiastic cheers of my men, I was the last to set foot on English soil, treading upon the land that was to become my kingdom.

[15] Furthermore, William was sure of the King of France's neutrality, for he was aged only 7 and William's father-in-law was his tutor.

Taking advantage of the English ost's distant northern position, I immediately had a castle built, while I inspected the surrounding area. Marshes! We needed to get out of there fast. We discovered a harbour town nestling in a coastal indentation – Hastings – where I transferred my ost. My half-brother Robert had wooden towers built there on mounds, which he surrounded with stockades and ditches.

A messenger informed me of Harold's approaching army, after his victory over the Norwegians. He had massacred thousands of Vikings, among them Tostig and the King of Norway. Hardrada's moribund fleet had retreated to the seas, hence bringing an end to the Viking era in England. However, Harold's army was weak…
In York, he had been informed of my landing on the 2nd of October. Two of his brothers, Gyrth and Leofwine, suggested he cut our supply lines. He stupidly urged on his troops. Exhausted by their recent combat, they travelled down England in forced marches. Entrenched, we began to ravage the land. Impatient, and without waiting for reinforcements, Harold left London on the 11th of October! Ha! Ha!

Soon, on the morning of the 13th of October, our patrols discovered English sentries watching over the road to Hastings. Harold sent an emissary to ask me to abandon my plans! Leave my own land! I refused! "May God be our judge," Harold concluded.

Our encounter was imminent. By day, certain enemy troops joined forces at a locality named "The Grey Apple Tree", whilst others headed for a nearby forest where they built a stockade. They gathered together on a hill in the evening. But, my own troops were well aware of their nocturnal movements. Cautious, we left them to deploy. Then Harold refused my latest proposals, bringing a halt to negotiations. The time had come. The crucial time.

The night had been short, and spirits were nervous. On the dawn of Saturday the 14th, the sun rose at 5.30am. Half an hour later,

after a church service, I put on my ring armour and gave orders to march ahead. My ost headed northwards. A gonfalonier rode alongside my thoroughbred horse, carrying the papal standard. Behind me, my squire followed, carrying my sword, then Odo, armed only with a club. I could hear the rear guard of my long column, the Bretons from the third army corps, electrified by the sound of bagpipes and bombards. I heard, above all, my ost singing, to chase the anguish that had seized the Flemish as far as Roger de Mongommery's troops and the Normans of Italy.

A scout soon informed me of the enemy position. We could no longer surprise them! Overnight, they had moved to the crest of a different hill. A defensive hill, where the enemy ranks were side by side, in several rows, behind a wall of Scandinavian warriors - eight hundred of Harold's elite guards in the form of Danish troops armed with massive war axes who surrounded seven thousand English peasants who were barely trained, barely armed, yet devoutly faithful to their king…

I raised my rod of command. Upon this order, my ost divided at the foot of the hill, under enemy eyes. For an hour, my troops gathered in battle order, the archers in front, the heavy artillery in the middle, wearing hauberks and armed with javelins and pikes, and the cavalry to the rear. Oh! My cavalry! Of which I was personally in command! I deployed them over three contingents: my Bretons, Angevins and Poitevins on the left wing, us in the centre, and my French, Picard and Flemish troops on the right wing. I had federated a great number of mercenaries under the Norman banner! With four thousand five hundred infantrymen, two thousand five hundred light cavalrymen and a thousand archers, our numbers were equal to those of our enemy. Not forgetting our three thousand horses. Half an hour later, my front line of archers approached the enemy… The terrifying sound of trumpets gave the signal to fight the "battle of the grey apple"! It was nine in the morning when the first salvo of arrows was fired…

Withered flower of the cavalry!

OUR FIRST ARROWS SHOWERED IN THOUSANDS, BUT MISSED THEIR TARGETS!

OUR POSITION IS TOO LOW TO FIRE!

THEIR QUIVERS EMPTY AFTER THIS FIRST DUEL, OUR ARCHERS WENT UNDER COVER TO ENABLE THE RANK AND FILE TO ATTACK. AS THEY CLIMBED UP THE SLOPE, THE LATTER WAS SHOWERED WITH STONES.

OUR EFFORTS ARE VAIN...

...SEND THE CAVALRY IN TO BACK THEM UP!

DEUS AÏEEEEE!!!

THEY ARE AT A STANDSTILL, UNABLE TO USE THEIR JAVELINS AND PIKES!

AND INCAPABLE OF THRUSTING INTO THE ENGLISH LINES!

THE HORSEMEN VIOLENTLY STRUCK THE MORTAL DANISH AXES AND LONG SHIELDS.

THEY DISPERSED, PANIC-STRICKEN, DISORGANISED...

THE CAVALRY IS WITH-DRAWING!

ANOTHER FAILURE!

THEIR RETREAT ON THE LEFT WING SET THE OTHER ARMY CORPS OFF-BALANCE AND THEY STAGGERED TOWARDS THE CENTRE AND THE RIGHT.

THE ENEMY WALL HASN'T MOVED AN INCH! MY NORMANS ARE FLEEING NOW! IT'S A ROUT!

I NEEDED TO LEAVE THE TELHAM HEIGHTS FROM WHERE I HAD BEEN WATCHING THE BATTLE WITH ODO.

I MUST HARANGUE THOSE RUNAWAYS!

AAH!!!

AT THAT PRECISE MOMENT, MY CHARGER FELL!

I HIT HIS HORSE, HAROLD! HE IS DEAD!

WELL DONE GYRTH!

A JAVELIN!

THE DUKE IS DEAD! SAVE YOUR SKINS!

QUICK, I MUST GET UP! FIND A HORSE!

LOOK AT ME, I AM ALIVE AND I WILL VANQUISH WITH GOD'S HELP!

I NEEDED TO BE TAKEN IN FRONT OF THE DESERTERS TO PUT PAID TO THE RUMOUR!

THE RUMOUR OF MY DEATH ACCENTUATED THE FRANTIC RETREAT!

AFTER MY PARADE, THE BATTLE RESUMED!

I REGAINED CONTROL, ADOPTING NEW TACTICS...

TURN LEFT! SURROUND THE ENGLISH PURSUERS!

LEADING MY PERSONAL GUARD, I BROUGHT MY CAVALRY TO SAVE THEM.

AS SEVERAL HUNDRED ENGLISH PEASANTS CHASED OUR BRETONS TO THE FOOT OF THE HILL, THE NORMAN CAVALRY HEADED FOR THE MARSHES WHERE THE BRETONS WERE BEING DRIVEN BACK.

BRETONS! RETURN TO COMBAT!!

ATTACK! ATTACK!

ODO'S TROOPS SOON MANAGED TO ENCIRCLE THE CARELESS ENGLISH PURSUERS ON AN OUTCROP.

THERE ARE MANY DEAD AMONG THE ENGLISH!

BUT THEY HAVE RETURNED TO THEIR HEIGHTS!

CURSED HILLOCK, WILL WE SUCCEED IN OUSTING OUT ITS OCCUPANTS?

WHEN THE SUN WAS AT ITS PEAK, A MOMENT'S RESPITE WAS NECESSARY. I REUNITED AND NOURISHED MY ARMY.

EXCELLENT! OUR NEW TACTIC IS PERFECT!

REORGANISED, MY OST EMBARKED ON A NEW ASSAULT ON THE WEST FLANK OF THE ENGLISH WALL.

BUT WE TURNED BACK, CHASED BY THE SAXONS WHO DISPERSED THEIR HILLSIDE LINES.

THEY'RE SOUNDING THE RETREAT!

AND ON MY RIGHT FLANK, COMMANDED BY ROBERT DE BEAUMONT...

TURN ROUND!

TURN TOWARDS THE ENGLISH LEFT WING!

AND STRIKE, STRIKE!

THE UNEXPECTED BRETON FLIGHT AND ITS HAPPY ENDING HAD INSPIRED US WITH OTHER FLIGHTS, PRETEND ONES...

THESE SUCCESSIVE COUNTER-ATTACKS ENDED UP DISBANDING THE ENEMY LINES.

THEN...

THE NORMANS ARE TURNING ROUND!!!

THEIR WING IS BROKEN! THE ENGLISH ARE RETREATING! AT LAST!!

TIGHTEN UP THE FRONT! THEIR RANKS ARE DIMINISHING!

DON'T LET THE WINGS SPREAD OUT!

IMMEDIATELY, OUR CAVALRY MADE A LIGHTNING CHARGE AND MASSACRED THE CARELESS SAXONS.

WHAT IN THE DEVIL! THE NORMANS ARE NOW TRYING TO PENETRATE INSIDE MY ARMY RANKS!

THE ELITE SOLDIERS ARE HOLDING STRONG! THE OUTCOME IS UNSURE!

WE MUST ADOPT A DIFFERENT STRATAGEM, BOULOGNE! ARGH...

SURROUNDED BY SOLDIERS WHO CLEARED THE WAY FOR ME AMIDST THE COMMOTION OF THE BATTLE, I MANAGED TO CATCH UP WITH MY OST'S REAR TROOPS.

FIRERS, GET AS CLOSE AS YOU CAN TO THE TOP OF THE HILL!

AS FOR THE OTHERS, TAKE UP POSITIONS AT THE BOTTOM OF THE SLOPE!

CAREFUL! VERTICAL ARROWS! CERTAIN ARCHERS ARE FIRING STRAIGHT ABOVE NOW!

PROTECT YOUR-SELVES!

THE REAR IS BEING DIVE-BOMBED WITH ARROWS! RAISE YOUR SHIELDS!

TAP!

TAP!

TAP!

TAP!

TAP!!

IMMEDIATELY, FROM THE HEIGHTS OF OUR OWN LINES, ARROWS WERE ALSO FIRED, HORIZONTALLY.

FIRE, FIRE!

THEIR ARCHERY CORPS HAS INFILTRATED OUR RANKS!

THEY ARE FIRING FLAT TRAJECTORY SHOTS!

CURSE THEM!

ARGH!

OUR ARROWS TARGETED THE ELITE TROOPS WHO, IN TURN, RAISED THEIR SHIELDS TO PROTECT FROM THE FIRST SHOTS.

OUR TACTIC IS WORKING! KEEP REPEATING IT! ORDER OTHER BURSTS OF FIRE!

THEY ARE FIRING HEAVILY! OUR FRONT IS BURSTING ON ITS RIGHT AND LEFT FLANKS, ATTACKED IN THE CENTRE!

WHAT...

HAAAAAAAAA!!

THEN, MY CAVALRY THRUST FORWARD, THROWING PROJECTILES, AVOIDING HAND-TO-HAND COMBAT. THEN OUR INFANTRYMEN ATTACKED. AND, LATE AFTERNOON...

THE WALL IS BROKEN! AT LAST!

LET'S HEAD FOR THEIR COMMAND POST!

HURRAY, MY FRIENDS! WE HAVE REACHED THE COMMAND POST!

THEIR KING IS WOUNDED, WILLIAM!

HAVE A COMMANDO OF HORSEMEN CLEAR A PATH TOWARDS HIM, TO FINISH HIM OFF!

EUSTACHE DE BOULOGNE, GAUTIER GIFFARD, HUGUES DE PONTHIEU, GO!

NEWS OF HAROLD'S DEATH SPREAD FROM MOUTH TO MOUTH AMONG THE ENEMY RANKS, WHILST REINFORCEMENTS IN THE FORM OF SAXON PEASANTS ARRIVED AT THE BATTLEFIELD.

ALL AROUND, THERE WAS FRANTIC RETREAT AND DESERTION OF COMMAND POSTS, WITH THE EXCEPTION OF THE ELITE INFANTRY CORPS WHICH CONTINUED TO FIGHT WITH THEIR LONG AXES HELD IN BOTH HANDS. THEY HAD ALL LOST CONFIDENCE, HOUNDED, ENCIRCLED TILL DAYBREAK.

THEN THE ARMY SPREAD OUT, FLEEING AMIDST THE UTMOST CONFUSION.

BY NIGHTFALL, I KNEW I WAS IN CONTROL OF THE BATTLEFIELD. THE PRIDE OF THE ANGLO-SAXON ARISTOCRACY WAS LYING AT MY FEET. THE ENGLISH THRONE WAS WITHIN REACH. APART FROM THE FAR TOO YOUNG EDGAR AETHELING, I HAD NO RIVALS.

WILLIAM! FRENCH HORSEMEN ARE TRAPPED IN A MARSHY RAVINE!

SOME HAVE HAD THEIR THROATS CUT BY THE ENGLISH DESERTERS!

FUTILE CARNAGE! STOP FIGHTING IMMEDIATELY!

IT WAS THE ULTIMATE SKIRMISH. IN THE EVENING, HEAVY SILENCE WAS UPON US. WE PACED UP AND DOWN THE BATTLEFIELD, COUNTING 5,000 DEAD IN THE BLOOD-STAINED HEATHER.

THEY HAVE LEFT THEIR KING, HAROLD, BEHIND!

SO, GOD HAS GIVEN HIS JUDG-MENT.

WE TOOK THE TIME TO REGAIN STRENGTH AROUND AN IMPROVISED CAMPFIRE...

WHEN I DECIDED ON THE OPERATION IN JANUARY, I HAD NO IDEA IT WOULD BE SUCH CARNAGE!

IT WAS A LONG BATTLE!

YES, IT USUALLY ONLY LASTS TWO HOURS!

WE FELL ASLEEP. FROM THE TOP OF THE HILL, I COULD DREAM OF OTHER HEIGHTS... MY MOTHER'S DREAM, THE ONE OF A TREE THAT COVERED ALL ENGLAND, COULD IT BE ABOUT TO COME TRUE?

WE BURIED OUR COMPANIONS THE NEXT DAY, AFTER RECOVERING THEIR HEAVY EQUIPMENT.

IN THE MORNING, WE LOOKED FOR ANY WOUNDED SOLDIERS. AT HASTINGS, I HAD LOST A THIRD OF MY OST.

THAT SUNDAY, A SURPRISE AWAITED ME...

I AM GYTHA, GODWIN'S WIDOW. I COME IN SEARCH OF MY POOR SON, HAROLD'S REMAINS. I OFFER YOU HIS WEIGHT IN GOLD IN EXCHANGE WILLIAM.

I DO NOT WANT YOUR GOLD! I GIVE YOU HIS BODY!

HAVE THE ENGLISH COME AND RECOVER THEIR DEAD!

A HIGH ALTAR WILL NEED TO BE BUILT ON THE SPOT WHERE HAROLD FELL...

THAT'S AN IDEA, ODO, AN IDEA...

I INDEED HAD THE HIGH ALTAR BUILT A FEW YEARS LATER. RIGHT NOW, MY CONQUEST COULD BEGIN!

AND THE GREY APPLE TREE BORE FRUIT

After my victory, my recomposed ost - suffering from dysentery - bypassed London, ravaging everything on its way, reinforced by another Norman army.

Uncompromising Stigand, Bishop of Winchester but nevertheless Archbishop of Canterbury, yielded to my authority. He had just crowned young Edgar Ætheling, vexing Earls Edwin and Morcar in the process. Hence, I ravaged the nation to force the aristocracy to surrender. With no hope, no leader, no troop, encircled London capitulated.

Merry Christmas 1066! I headed for the Church of St. Peter in the morning. "Duke William, by the glory of God, I Ealdred, Archbishop of York, place on your forehead the crown that makes you King of England!"

Then Odo blessed the goblets of spiced wine and the dishes that were served at the banquet, during which we conversed on all subjects, from the throes of our campaign to the promised division of fiefs.

I shared the land belonging to the Anglo-Saxon lords slain during my conquest with my vassals and allies. I pacified spirits, restored public safety and listened to the people. I treated young Ætheling, submitted to me, with respect.

At the end of my conquest, I reunited the duchy of Normandy and the kingdom of England under my sole authority. Vanquished, the Anglo-Saxon elite disappeared, leaving way for our own aristocracy, which brought its own language and culture.

Then I returned to Normandy. At the Abbey of Fécamp, I solemnly celebrated Easter in April 1067. Ah! My duchy was full of joy! Formerly "Bastard", I had just earned a new epithet, at the point of the sword: that of Conqueror. In February, I had entrusted the administration of my conquered land to Odo and William FitzOsbern. On my guard, I had also taken high English dignitaries with me on my triumphal journey.

Then in September, as Matilda's stomach was beginning to swell once more, my father-in-law, Baldwin, died. As Count of Flanders, he had offered me ships and troops for my conquest.

After nine months in peaceful Normandy, the triumphal march came to an end one 6th of December. After having entrusted Matilda and my eldest son Robert with my duchy, I had to return to my new kingdom to establish my own bailiffs. Hence, in their respective castles, they could all keep a watchful eye over the coast...

THE ACRID SMELL OF REBELLIOUS LANDS

THE NEWS IS BAD. UPRISINGS HAVE BROKEN OUT IN EXETER AND HEREFORD!

THE WELSH DEVASTATED HEREFORDSHIRE IN AUGUST!

ODO AND WILLIAM FITZOSBERN!

THEY PROVOKED THIS REBELLION BY REFUSING TO DO JUSTICE TO THE ENGLISH WHO WERE OPPRESSED BY OUR OFFICERS!

TO CONTROL THE COUNTRY, THEY HAVE BUILT FORTRESSES FROM WHERE OTHER NORMANS MAINTAIN PEACE OVER THE SURROUNDING REGIONS.

THE BATTLE HAS BEEN WON, WILLIAM, BUT NOT THE WAR!

ROGER ...

I GIVE YOU THE RAPE OF ARUNDEL, INCLUDING THE CITY OF CHICHESTER, TWO ESSENTIAL SITES FOR DEFENDING THE SOUTH OF THE KINGDOM!

IN ARUNDEL...

...ROGER IMMEDIATELY HAD A HILL ERECTED TO BUILD A CASTRAL MOUND, WHICH WAS SOON COMPLETED WITH A BARRACK-ROOM IN 1070.

I TOOK EXETER, AT THE HEART OF THE REBELLION, AFTER A SHORT SIEGE IN JANUARY AND FEBRUARY 1068.

ADELA!

OOUiiNN!!

SOON, MY RETURN TO NORMANDY WAS TO COINCIDE WITH A PRECIOUS GIFT, HEADED WITH A ROYAL CROWN – MATILDA GAVE BIRTH TO MY LITTLE PRINCESS, THE YOUNGEST OF MY DAUGHTERS!

I CELEBRATED EASTER IN WINCHESTER ON THE 23RD OF MARCH...

...ON WHIT SUNDAY, LATE MAY 1068, MATILDA, WHO WAS EXPECTING AGAIN, WAS CROWNED QUEEN.

BUT IN THE SUMMER OF 1068, AN ENGLISH REVOLT BROKE OUT IN NORTHUMBRIA.

THE ANGLO-SAXON TROOP MARCHED SOUTHWARDS...

BUT BROKE UP AS SOON AS WE ATTEMPTED ANY COUNTER-ATTACK!

THE SAME SUMMER, HAROLD'S TWO SONS, GODWIN II AND MAGNUS OF WESSEX, LANDED IN EXETER WITH MERCENARIES FROM THE IRISH KING'S FLEET FROM LEINSTER.

ANOTHER DEFEAT FOR THEM!

THEN, WILLIAM FITZOSBERN REPRESSED REBELLIONS IN SHREWSBURY AND EXETER.

NOT FORGETTING, ANOTHER HAPPY EVENT...

THE ARRIVAL OF MY YOUNGEST SON, HENRY, BORN IN THE AUTUMN.

HAVING VERY LITTLE CONTROL OVER THE MIDLANDS AND NORTHERN ENGLAND, I INITIATED A CAMPAIGN TO BUILD FORTRESSES THERE.

IN THE NORTH OF ENGLAND, A NEW REVOLT BROKE OUT EARLY 1069.

ROBERT DE COMINES' ARMY HAD ENTERED DURHAM, DESPITE WARNINGS FROM A BISHOP OF THE RAISING OF AN ANGLO-SAXON ARMY.

ON THE 28TH OF JANUARY, THE ENGLISH ARMY SEIZED THE CITY, ANNIHILATING MY ARMY.

A TRAGIC ERROR!

COMINES HAS TAKEN REFUGE WITH THE BISHOP!

BURN HIM!

IN FEBRUARY, THE PUGNACIOUS ARMY ATTACKED YORK, THE PRINCIPAL NORTHERN TOWN. THERE, AFTER FORCING THE LOCAL POPULATION TO SUPPORT ÆTHELING, THEY KILLED THE NORMAN GARRISON AND THEIR LORD WITH THEM!

INFORMED OF THE SCALE OF THE REVOLT, I HAD NO CHOICE BUT TO SEVERELY REPRESS.

THE IRISH KING LOANED THE DUBLIN FLEET TO GODWIN II AND MAGNUS OF WESSEX...

AND ON THE 24TH OF JUNE...

SIXTY SHIPS!

I RECONQUERED YORK, WHERE I HAD A SECOND FORTRESS BUILT...

WILLIAM FITZOSBERN, I ENTRUST YOU WITH THIS CASTLE!

THEN, AS OSBERN SET TO PACIFYING THE NORTH, I RETURNED TO WINCHESTER, WHERE I CELEBRATED EASTER.

THEY LANDED IN THE SOUTHWEST OF THE KINGDOM AND ATTACKED EXETER.

OSBERN IS PUTTING UP GOOD RESISTANCE IN HIS NEW CASTLE!

BEATEN! HAROLD'S SONS ARE BEATEN! ONCE MORE!

FRUSTRATED BY THIS SECOND DEFEAT, THEY ORGANISED RAIDS IN CORNWALL.

WORSE, IN AUGUST...

AN IMMENSE DANISH AND NORWEGIAN FLEET, COMMANDED BY THE DANISH KING'S TWO BROTHERS, APPEARED ON THE WESTERN COAST.

REALISING THAT THE REVOLT LED BY ÆTHELING WAS VAIN, THE ENGLISH CHIEFS HAD PROMISED THE THRONE TO SWEYN ESTRIDSSEN, THE KING OF DENMARK!

ONCE THEY HAD LANDED ON THE SOUTHEAST COAST, THE DANES SAILED ALONG THE COAST, TESTING THE NORMAN DEFENCES, BEFORE ANCHORING IN THE CALM RIVER HUMBER ON THE 8TH OF SEPTEMBER.

WHERE THEY JOINED FORCES WITH ÆTHELING AND WALTHEOF'S ENGLISH TROOPS.

TOGETHER, THEY RECONQUERED YORK ON THE 21ST...

LET'S RAZE THEIR TWO CASTLES TO THE GROUND!

WALTHEOF JUBILANTLY DECAPITATED OUR HUNDRED NORMANS AS THEY TRIED, ONE BY ONE, TO LEAVE OUR FORTS!

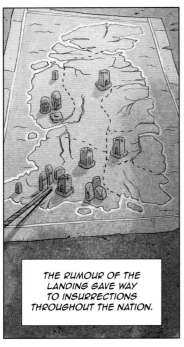

THE RUMOUR OF THE LANDING GAVE WAY TO INSURRECTIONS THROUGHOUT THE NATION.

BUT THE REBELS DID NOT SEEK TO TAKE ADVANTAGE OF MY WORST DEFEAT IN ENGLAND. THEIR MISTAKE!

BETTER STILL, THE RUMOUR OF MY ARRIVAL HAS GENERATED FRANTIC RETREAT.

I HAVE COME IN PERSON TO REPRESS THIS UPRISING. I SHALL RETURN TO THE NORTH WHILE MY HALF-BROTHER ROBERT AND ROBERT OF EU KEEP WATCH OVER THE DANES IN THE HUMBER!

THEN, AT A STANDSTILL FOR THREE WEEKS DUE TO A COLLAPSED BRIDGE OVER THE RIVER AIRE, I WAS UNABLE TO ATTACK YORK, STILL IN DANISH HANDS.

SO I REPEATED MY THREE YEAR-OLD LONDON STRATEGY...

...DEVASTATING, IN DECEMBER, A VAST BAND OF TERRITORY AROUND THE CITY, TO ISOLATE IT.

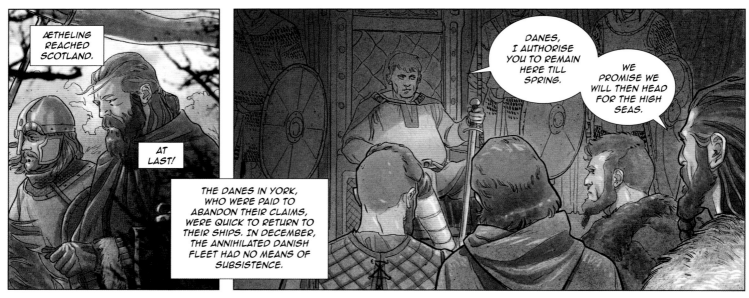

ÆTHELING REACHED SCOTLAND.

AT LAST!

THE DANES IN YORK, WHO WERE PAID TO ABANDON THEIR CLAIMS, WERE QUICK TO RETURN TO THEIR SHIPS. IN DECEMBER, THE ANNIHILATED DANISH FLEET HAD NO MEANS OF SUBSISTENCE.

DANES, I AUTHORISE YOU TO REMAIN HERE TILL SPRING.

WE PROMISE WE WILL THEN HEAD FOR THE HIGH SEAS.

I ALSO EXPROPRIATED THE ANGLO-SAXON ARISTOCRATS, WHO PREFERRED EXILE...

...REPLACING THEM WITH NORMAN NOBILITY.

AFTER THE CHRISTMAS CELEBRATIONS, I RESUMED MY DEVASTATION CAMPAIGN IN NORTHUMBRIA, STILL HEADING NORTHWARDS...

SOMETHING I'M NOT PROUD OF TODAY...

TOTALLY DESTITUTE, IN THE MIDST OF THE WINTER, THE SURVIVORS SUCCUMBED IN MASSES, FORCED TO EAT DOGS AND CATS TO ESCAPE FAMINE...

OR WORSE...

I FEEL REMORSE, I ADMIT...

AT THE MOUTH OF THE TEES, I OBTAINED WALTHEOF AND GOSPATRICK OF NORTHUMBRIA'S SUBMISSION.

IN FEBRUARY, TO PERFECT MY CONQUEST, I TOOK MY OST TO THE PENNINE MOUNTAINS.

DESPITE YOUR EXHAUSTION, WE MUST HEAD FOR MERCIA, WHERE THE REMAINING REBELS BEATEN AT STAFFORD HAVE RETREATED!

IT HAS BEEN A TOUGH CAMPAIGN! TOO TOUGH!

WE, BRETON AND ANGEVIN SOLDIERS, REQUEST THAT YOU RELEASE US FROM SERVICE, WILLIAM!

AFTER STIFLING THE VERY LAST POCKET, I LIBERATED MY ARMY IN SALISBURY, IN SOUTHERN ENGLAND, BEFORE EASTER.

I FEARED MUTINY!

IT IS A WISE DECISION!

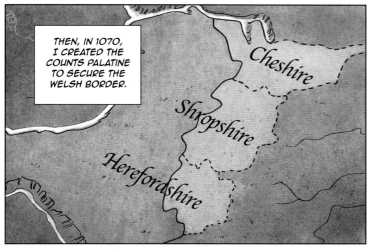

THEN, IN 1070, I CREATED THE COUNTS PALATINE TO SECURE THE WELSH BORDER.

Cheshire

Shropshire

Herefordshire

WILLIAM FITZOSBERN BUILT CHEPSTOW CASTLE ALONG WITH OTHER STRONGHOLDS.

THEN HE WON BATTLES WITH THREE WELSH KINGS, WHICH ENABLED HIM TO MULTIPLY HIS POSSESSIONS.

ONCE MORE, IT WAS AT EASTER IN 1070 THAT I WAS CROWNED KING OF ENGLAND...

...IN THE PRESENCE OF THREE PAPAL LEGATES.

DURING THE OCTAVE OF EASTER, I GATHERED A COUNCIL IN WINCHESTER AND DEPOSED THE ARCHBISHOP OF CANTERBURY ALONG WITH OTHER BISHOPS WHO WERE NOT ACKNOWLEDGED BY ROME...

...TO REPLACE HIM WITH LANFRANC IN AUGUST.

NAMED PRIMATE OF ENGLAND IN 1072, LANFRANC ENDEAVOURED TO MAINTAIN THE INDEPENDENCE OF THE ANGLICAN CHURCH WHILST REFORMING IT, ABOLISHING THE WORSHIP OF MANY SAINTS.

AFTER THE FIRST UPRISINGS, I ESTABLISHED NEW ABBOTS AND BISHOPS THROUGHOUT MY KINGDOM, THE MAJORITY OF WHOM WERE NORMAN OR FRENCH.

THESE ADMINISTRATORS ORGANISED CHAPTERS AND BUILT NEW PRIORIES.

SWEYN, THE KING OF DENMARK, LED A FLEET.

BUT, ON THE 2ND OF JUNE...

OUSTED OUT IN FEBRUARY, THE DANES HAD RETURNED TO OUR COAST.

THEY PILLAGED THE MONASTERY IN PETERBOROUGH.

LET'S TAKE THEIR TREASURE TO ELY.

AT THE END OF THE MONTH, SWEYN AND I AGREED THAT THE DANISH FLEET WOULD LEAVE THE ENGLISH WATERS, TAKING WITH IT ITS MONASTIC BOOTY.

I WAS A GOOD SOVEREIGN.

REPENTANT, I HAD EVEN HAD AN ABBEY BUILT ON THE SITE OF THE BATTLE OF HASTINGS.

BELLIGERENT NEIGHBOURS ALL AROUND

I was then to face several interior revolts along with uprisings among neighbouring principalities, a prelude to the next two decades of my reign. My territory was expanding and I could no longer intervene at the necessary speed. And besides Normandy which was enjoying times of peace, I had accumulated military setbacks.

Early 1071, William FitzOsbern came back to Normandy to help Matilda govern the duchy, to watch over the war of succession in Flanders and to support Arnoul, the Flemish county's legitimate heir, against his uncle Robert the Frisian who had usurped the territory. During an ambush in Cassel, Robert the Frisian took William FitzOsbern's troop by surprise, killing FitzOsbern on the 20th of February. Hence, I had lost not only my most faithful companion, but also - should I admit? – my only friend.

In October 1071, after having launched a siege in Cambridge in April, I conquered Ely, the last pocket of English resistance. Most of Hereward the Wake's partisans, including Morcar, were taken prisoner. His brother Edwin was killed by his own army. Many of the prisoners were mutilated and blinded. Something I now regret.

Then in November, I entrusted Montgommery with the new and troubled county of Shropshire. Along with the Palatine powers, he protected my kingdom against Welsh incursions and had several castles built. Wise forethought. In July 1072, King Malcolm of Scotland entered England. Master of the kingdom, I nevertheless re-established order and the Scottish king's surrender in the autumn of 1072, hence completing my pacification campaign.

I was grateful to those who had faithfully assisted me. My pacified kingdom comprised seven principalities, each divided into counties. I relied much on Lanfranc and Geoffrey de Montbray. Henceforth, my nobility grew richer, by despoiling the Saxon lords, I can but admit.

Finally, twenty of my faithful followers shared half of the English territory. Having obtained vast territories, Odo was the richest lord in the kingdom, the only others who vaguely approached his wealth being his brother Robert and Roger de Montgommery.

My brother, the Count Robert of Mortain, became the second richest lord in England after my other brother Odo. He received vast estates throughout the kingdom, dominating Cornwall, Devon, Dorset and Somerset, strategically positioned to control the roads to London, Northamptonshire and Yorkshire. But also the strategic rape of Pevensey of which he occupied the castle since Hastings.

The deceased William FitzOsbern, the first Earl of Hereford, had been the fourth richest Anglo-Norman lord, which had enabled him to endow the two Norman abbeys he had founded, Lyre circa 1050 and Cormeilles circa 1060. He was named Earl as from 1067, exerting, from Winchester, his authority on all the southern counties where Harold himself had been earl.

Faithful Roger de Montgommery, the son of a viscount from Exmes, became the first Earl of Shrewsbury in 1074 and was among the six most powerful lords in England. Over and above a major share of Sussex, including the rape of Arundel, he owned seigniories that were among the most strategic in the kingdom.

And I didn't forget my assassinated tutors' children. Gilbert de Brionne's eldest son Richard Fitz Gislebert, was named Lord of Clare and Tonbridge to compensate for the fief of Brionne. William Fitz Gislebert, his younger brother, became Viscount of Devonshire. Two of Osbern the Steward's sons were also rewarded - William as Earl of Hereford and Osbern as Bishop of Exeter. The Grandemesnils, of whom Hugues, had fought at Hastings and were rewarded with one hundred fiefs including, in particular, the viscountcy of Leicestershire. What a turnaround for those from whom I had once confiscated the worldly goods, when they had fallen victim to Mabel de Bellême's hatred...

Henceforth, trade between the continent and my new kingdom intensified, Normandy's wheat and, of course, our beautiful Caen stone, were exported from Ouistreham. On the flanks of the valleys, the vast centuries old quarries of the Vaucelles district took advantage of the natural stone outcrop and of the nearby river, an affordable transport solution.

I was soon to look after my quarrelsome neighbour, Maine, against which I had launched a military campaign in 1073. Four years previously, the region's lords had ousted me out with support from the Count of Anjou. Although he bore the title of Count of Maine, my eldest son did not join the expedition. I had not deemed his presence necessary. My victory ensured Norman reoccupation of the county. There were belligerent neighbours everywhere. And everywhere, they had submitted to me. Everywhere? No...

DESPOILED COUNTS AND CHOPPED FEET

IN THE SPRING OF 1075, I RETURNED TO NORMANDY, CONFIDENT.

MISTAKE.

REBELLION WAS IN THE AIR AMONG THE ENGLISH EARLS!

MY DAUGHTER CECILIA, A NUN AT THE HOLY TRINITY IN CAEN, TOOK HER BENEDICTINE VOWS THERE.

AT EASTER, I TRAVELLED TO THE ABBEY OF THE HOLY TRINITY IN FÉCAMP, ONE OF THE MOST IMPORTANT SEIGNIORIES IN MY DUCHY.

CECILIA CAN TAKE INSTRUCTION HERE. OUR LIBRARY BOASTS AROUND 80 MANUSCRIPTS.

SO MANY?

YES! IT'S QUITE UNIQUE!

ALTHOUGH I HAVE OFFERED NO GOODS TO YOUR ABBEY SINCE 1059, I REMAIN VERY ATTACHED TO IT, ABBOT JEAN!

THE EVENT THAT REUNITES US TODAY IS FINE PROOF OF THAT!

AND US TOO, MY LORD! I AM BUT YOUR VASSAL. DUKES RICHARD I AND II WERE GENEROUS WITH ME. WE OWE THEM OUR RESURRECTION.

IN FÉCAMP, MEASURES WERE TAKEN AGAINST PRIVATE VENGEANCE AND WARFARE.

I FORBID ANY MAN TO ATTACK ANOTHER, UNLESS IT IS FOR THE MURDER OF HIS FATHER OR HIS SON.

IS THE ENGLISH SITUATION REALLY THAT UNSURE, WILLIAM?

YES! DURING MY ABSENCE, RALPH DE GAEL AND ROGER FITZ OSBERN, TWO OF THE SEVEN LORDS,

TRIED TO ISOLATE THE CENTRE OF THE KINGDOM WITH SUPPORT FROM BRETON MERCENARIES!

THANKFULLY, WALTHEOF, THE EARL OF NORTHAMPTON, REFUSED TO JOIN THE CONSPIRACY!

AFTER THE LOSS OF MY DAUGHTER AGATHA IN 1074 AT THE AGE OF TEN, RICHARD, THE SECOND OF MY FOUR SONS...

WAS KILLED IN 1075 IN A HUNTING ACCIDENT IN THE NEW FOREST.

HE WAS ONLY SIXTEEN!

HIS DEATH DRASTICALLY DISRUPTED OUR PLANS, MATILDA AND I...

WILLIAM, OUR THIRD SON, HAD TO DATE BEEN UNDER LANFRANC'S PROTECTION IN THE MEN'S ABBEY...

HE NOW SERVED ME AS A KNIGHT AND PROVED GOOD AND RESPECTFUL, LOYAL AND FAITHFUL TO HIS FATHER.

IN 1075, ROGER DE BRETEIL, THE POWERFUL EARL OF HEREFORD, ARRANGED THE MARRIAGE BETWEEN HIS SISTER EMMA AND THE BRETON RAOUL, BARON OF GAËL AND EARL OF NORFOLK AND SUFFOLK.

DURING THE NUPTIAL CELEBRATIONS, HELD NEAR NEWMARKET, ROGER JOINED AN ANGLO-BRETON CONSPIRACY AGAINST ME, DEVISED BY RALPH, BOTH MEN DISCONTENTED TO SEE THEIR POWER REDUCED BY MY ROYAL OFFICERS. WHAT TURNCOATS!

ONCE BACK IN HEREFORDSHIRE, ROGER RAISED AN ARMY, WORD OF WHICH REACHED ENGLAND'S TWO CHIEF LAWMEN, RICHARD DE BIENFAITE AND WILLIAM DE WARENNE.

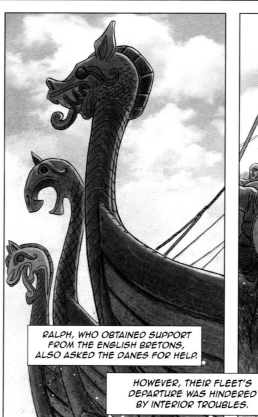

RALPH, WHO OBTAINED SUPPORT FROM THE ENGLISH BRETONS, ALSO ASKED THE DANES FOR HELP.

HOWEVER, THEIR FLEET'S DEPARTURE WAS HINDERED BY INTERIOR TROUBLES.

HE ALSO KINDLED IDEAS OF REBELLION AMONGST HIS ALLIES IN BRITTANY, WHO WERE READY TO OVERTURN THEIR DUKE AND ENTER MY DUCHY!

SINCE THE EARLS DID NOT DEIGN TO ACCEPT A SUMMONS FROM THE ROYAL COURT, BIENFAITE AND WARENNE HAD THE OST IN ENGLAND SENT TO CHALLENGE RALPH'S ARMY...

OUR TROOPS EASILY DEFEATED ROGER'S, HENCE PREVENTING THEM FROM JOINING FORCES WITH RALPH'S ARMY. ROGER WAS CAPTURED AND I HAD HIM THROWN IN PRISON. A TOTAL DISASTER, THE EARLS' CONSPIRACY!

LATER, LANFRANC TRIED TO CONVINCE ROGER TO MAKE AN ACT OF CONTRITION.

IN VAIN.

WHAT INGRATITUDE! ALL HE DID WAS INHERIT THE ESTATES I HAD OFFERED TO HIS FATHER!

THE REBELS CAPTURED DURING THE REVOLT WERE DESTINED TO AN UNENVIABLE FATE ...

CHOP OFF THEIR RIGHT FOOT!

WE'RE SURE TO RECOGNISE THEM LATER!

THE BLOODY REPRISAL BY THE OST IN ENGLAND BROUGHT VICTORY AGAINST RALPH IN NORFOLK.

FROM NORWICH, RALPH EMBARKED FOR BRITTANY, LEAVING HIS WIFE BEHIND INSIDE HIS BESIEGED CASTLE!

WHEN THEIR LAND WAS CONFISCATED, SHE JOINED HER HUSBAND, DEPOSED OF HIS TITLE OF EARL.

I PUSHED BACK THE FLEET BEFORE YORKSHIRE!

IN THE WINTER OF 1075, A DANISH FLEET THAT HAD COME TO SUPPORT THE EARLS APPROACHED THE ENGLISH COAST, BUT WHEN THEY REALISED THE REBELLION HAD FAILED, THEY HEADED FOR YORK.

CHRISTMAS 1075, WALTHEOF RETURNED TO ENGLAND WITH ME TO FINALLY BE ARRESTED, SUCH WAS MY SUSPICION OF HIS INVOLVEMENT IN THE EARLS' CONSPIRACY.

AFTER CONFESSING THE INTRIGUE TO LANFRANC, HE HAD COME TO NORMANDY TO ADMIT HIS FAULT.

FOOLISHNESS? COWARDICE? MANIPULATION?

I WAS TAKEN ABACK, I HAD GREAT ESTEEM FOR HIM...

ROGER DE BRETEIL WAS SENTENCED...

...TO THE LOSS OF HIS FIEFS AND LIFE IMPRISONMENT.

HENCEFORTH, HE OBSTINATELY AND INCESSANTLY INSULTED ME...

...I, WHO WAS NOW ABSOLUTE MASTER OF A PEACEFUL ENGLAND.

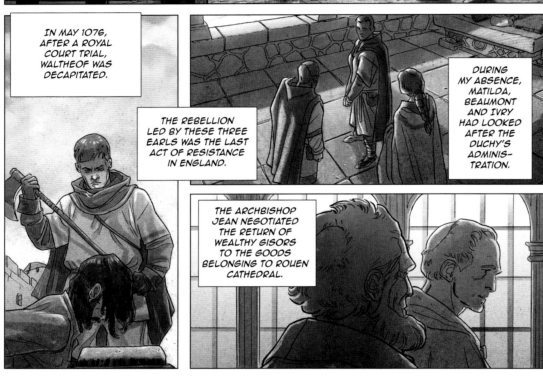

IN MAY 1076, AFTER A ROYAL COURT TRIAL, WALTHEOF WAS DECAPITATED.

THE REBELLION LED BY THESE THREE EARLS WAS THE LAST ACT OF RESISTANCE IN ENGLAND.

DURING MY ABSENCE, MATILDA, BEAUMONT AND IVRY HAD LOOKED AFTER THE DUCHY'S ADMINIS-TRATION.

THE ARCHBISHOP JEAN NEGOTIATED THE RETURN OF WEALTHY GISORS TO THE GOODS BELONGING TO ROUEN CATHEDRAL.

THE ESTATE HAD BEEN GRANTED, TILL THE END OF HIS LIFE, TO SIMON DE VEXIN'S FATHER, WHO HAD DIED THE PREVIOUS YEAR.

ITS REINSTATEMENT MEANT THE RETURN OF A STRATEGIC FIEF ON THE BORDER OF THE DUCHY.

AT THE SAME PERIOD, THE NORMAN KNIGHTS MAINTAINED IN ENGLAND BECAME WEARY...

IF MY HUSBAND DOES NOT HURRY HOME, I SHALL OFFER MYSELF TO ANOTHER!

SO WILL I!

...AS DID THEIR WIVES, ABANDONED IN NORMANDY. VIA FREQUENT LETTERS, SOME OF THEM DEMANDED THEIR RETURN!

CONSE-QUENTLY, MANY KNIGHTS ARE RETURNING TO THE DUCHY.

ON THE 14TH OF OCTOBER 1076, THE ARRIVAL OF PHILIP I IN BRITTANY FORCED ME TO PUT AN END TO MY SIEGE OVER THE BRETON CONSPIRATORS IN DOL.

THE FOLLOWING YEAR, BOOSTED BY HIS VICTORY, THE KING OF FRANCE SEIZED THE VEXIN COUNTY.

I GAVE UP ON BRITTANY, WHERE RALPH BECAME A POWERFUL LORD AND SIGNED AN ACT OF PEACE IN 1077 WITH PHILIP I.

ALTHOUGH I HAD TO GIVE WAY IN BRITTANY, MY 25 YEAR-OLD DAUGHTER CONSTANCE NEVERTHELESS MARRIED ALAN IV OF CORNOUAILLE, DUKE OF BRITTANY. EXCELLENT REVENGE!

CURSED RALPH DE GAEL!

I MUST FLEE! HE CAN PLOT ALL HE LIKES, I WILL NEVER GIVE HIM BACK THE COUNTY OF NORFOLK!

THE NORMAN PRELATES WERE JOYFULLY WELCOMED ON THEIR RETURN FROM ROME.

IN BAYEUX, ON THE 14TH OF JULY 1077, THE CATHEDRAL WAS SOLEMNLY CONSECRATED BY ODO.

THE CATHEDRAL IS FINALLY COMPLETE, ODO!

YOU HAVE WORKED ADMIRABLY FOR YOUR DIOCESE AND HAVE EXTENDED ITS CHAPTER.

NOT QUITE WHAT YOU HAD IN MIND WHEN YOU DECIDED TO REINFORCE YOUR AUTHORITY OVER BESSIN BY SETTING HANDS ON THIS LUCRATIVE BISHOPRIC?

AS YOU KNOW WILLIAM, MOST IMPORTANTLY, I FUNDED RECONSTRUCTION OF THE CATHEDRAL AND THE EPISCOPAL PALACE!

I HAVE ALSO SPONSORED MANY CLERICS.

AMONG THEM, VITAL, FOUNDER OF THE ORDER OF SAVIGNY, AN ABBOT FROM FÉCAMP AND AN ARCHBISHOP FROM YORK.

UPON MY ARRIVAL, THE EPISCOPAL HERITAGE, WHICH HAD ONCE BEEN USURPED DURING THE SCANDINAVIAN COLONISATION, WAS RECOVERED!

AN INSUBORDINATE ELDEST SON

The same year, an incident occurred in L'Aigle. A decisive incident that inflamed the situation. With no territory, my eldest son Robert, Count of Maine and heir to the duchy of Normandy, was frustrated to have no power and no personal resources. Unsure of his leadership qualities, I had chosen not to share my authority with him, for he was a liberal and frivolous lord who lived a life of great luxury.

On a visit to L'Aigle, my younger sons William and Henry paid a visit to Robert. After playing dice on a terrace, the two brothers urinated from an upper floor over their elder brother and his friends. "Your scornful brothers have covered us with filth! Why suffer such outrage? If you do not punish them, you will never rise above them!", Robert's companions told him, as he prepared to reprimand my younger sons. As I tried to calm him down, my eldest son screamed at me, "I claim Normandy!" – "Over my dead body!" I retorted, offended. Robert, vexed, secretly slipped away with his men, evading my cavalry and heading for Rouen where he tried to take control of the castle. In vain. The fortress's vigilant governor was on the lookout. Furious, I rushed to Rouen where I ordered for Robert to be arrested.

But he had already left the duchy. Robert de Bellême, of bad advice, had set him against his me, in total contrast with his father, Roger de Montgommery who was my own faithful adviser.

Robert sought refuge with Hugues de Châteauneuf, a hereditary enemy of the Dukes of Normandy and vassal to the Count of Perche, Rotrou. Robert and his companions took up residence in the Rémalard castral mound, protected by ditches and located on the banks of the Huisne. Although my initial plan was to fight against Rotrou, I decided to buy him. Rotrou was totally deaf but could still succumb to the heady smell of money... and he took me to Rémalard.

In 1077, during the conquest of the seigniory of Bellême, led in the company of my new ally, I besieged the fortress which was defended by Robert's last remaining partisans. Around the site, I had four fortified mounds built which I occupied with intrepid troops to put a stop to any attempt to help the rebels. Bellême was equipped with weapons, victuals and soldiers, hence the length of its siege. However, one day its defender escorted the King of France's grand master, leaving his castle walls in the company of three knights. Mistake! Four of my own knights saw him, then rushed to kill him. They loaded his blood-bathed body onto one of their horses and took him back to Rémalard, where they threw him in front of his father, Roger de Montgommery. When he learned of his father's slaughter, young Guillaume de Villeray, still besieged, feared for his own life. So finally, after having parleyed with him, I took control of Bellême. Now devoid of resources, the rebellion ceased.

However, my eldest son sought refuge with his uncle, Robert the Frisian, then with the King of France's court. Two of my enemies! Supporting Robert in his revolt, a crowd of young knights fled with him. Their land was confiscated, Conches in particular. Yet, I believed the most important problem to be elsewhere! Robert became a nightmare!

Soon, I was brought incredible news: "Gerberoy? On the Norman frontier? That stronghold has been entrusted to Robert?" By leaving it to my son, the King of France hoped to diminish the Norman power! In December 1078, cut to the quick, I began a long siege of the city, perched on a hilltop in the Pays de Bray, in the confines of Normandy and of France.

Then, over the winter of 1078-1078, Philip I reversed his allegiance and came to Étampes to join me in the siege. Late January, I was still besieging my eldest son, entrenched in his Château des Vidames. A defeat for me, King of England, held in check by my own son. A double defeat. Personal. Worse, we confronted each other, weapons in hand, over a quite singular duel. Robert even wounded me, knocking me off my horse with his spear. Wounded by my own son! Even if only slightly wounded, a distressing experience.

Finally, via the treaty of Gerberoy, thanks to the King of France's support, Robert obtained the administration of Normandy upon my death. And I feel the day approaching my friends...

My deprived eldest son led a nomad life until help came from his mother, who had remained very close to him and who, pained by our rivalry, had taken the habit of sending him money and gold. When I learned of this, I angrily threatened Matilda's Breton messenger with physical cruelty. Then, saddened, I made peace with Robert in 1080. Despite our reconciliation, the Gerberoy episode changed the fate of my youngest son William, at the expense of his elder brother. Having said that, Robert did finally obtain responsibilities. But only in England, alongside his uncle, Odo, where he had Newcastle castle built to contain the Scots. My son William came to England with me to take part in a few campaigns in Wales and in Scotland which I, in turn, ravaged to force its governors to negotiate. Decidedly, wherever there is land, there is war.

A PERIOD OF DISILLUSION

ON THE ISLE OF WIGHT, DURING THE WINTER OF 1082, ODO RAISED AN ARMY IN THE AIM OF ORGANISING A MILITARY EXPEDITION TO ROME.

POPE GREGORY VII IS GOING THROUGH DIFFICULT TIMES – THE PERFECT OPPORTUNITY TO SEIZE THE CHAIR OF SAINT PETER.

ODO, MY REGULAR DEPUTY IN ENGLAND, COULD ACT UPON HIS PERSONAL INITIATIVE AT ANY TIME, WITH THE EQUIVALENT OF ROYAL AUTHORITY ...

ALTHOUGH WILLIAM NAMED ME VICE-KING A FEW MONTHS AGO, SECONDING HIM IN LONDON IS NO LONGER OF INTEREST TO ME! I WILL BE POPE! I AM SURE OF VOTES FROM CARDINALS AND HAVE OBTAINED THAT CURTHOSE, WILLIAM'S HEIR, PLEAD MY CAUSE!

AT LAST! I WILL BE MORE POWERFUL THAN LANFRANC, THE PRIMATE OF ENGLAND!

I CAME TO ARREST HIM.

I AM CONDEMNING NEITHER CLERIC NOR BISHOP! I ARREST THE EARL OF KENT!

I ACCUSE HIM OF TREASON!

I ACCUSE HIM OF HAVING OPPRESSED ENGLAND BY MULTIPLYING ACTS OF VIOLENCE AND BY DESPOILING THE POOR!

AS POWERFUL A BISHOP HE WAS, THE MAN WHO HAD URGED CURTHOSE INTO REBELLION WAS IMPRISONED IN ROUEN.

HIS ENGLISH POSSESSIONS WERE CONFISCATED!

WHAT A REVERSE OF FORTUNE FOR HE WHO HAD FOUNDED THE ABBEY OF SAINT-VIGOR-LE-GRAND, THE SITE OF HIS FUTURE SEPULCHRE!

FURTHER ESTRANGEMENT WITH MY ELDEST SON CAME IN 1083. CURTHOSE PREFERRED TO LEAVE THE COURT AND GO INTO EXILE IN ITALY.

I HAVE NEVER SEEN HIM SINCE.

HE THEN SOUGHT HIS FORTUNE AT THE ROYAL COURT OF FRANCE.

ALTHOUGH SUPPOSEDLY OWNED BY ROBERT, MY ELDEST SON, WHO WAS MARRIED TO THE COUNT OF MAINE'S DAUGHTER, MAINE DETACHED ITSELF FROM MY INFLUENCE!

AFTER A SHORT CAMPAIGN, I HAD SUBMITTED THE REGION IN 1073. OR AT LEAST, I THOUGHT SO...

MY POWERFUL ARMY HAD CAPTURED CASTLES THAT WERE OWNED BY HUBERT DE BEAUMONT ...

I WILL SEEK REVENGE! I WILL RAISE A KEEP IN SAINTE-SUZANNE, BEAUMONT'S WORD!

IN 1083, ENTRENCHED IN SAINTE-SUZANNE WITH HIS FAMILY, BEAUMONT CHALLENGED ME. SO I SET OFF ON CAMPAIGN...

HE IS BITTERLY DEFENDING.

THEN THIS INSUBORDINATE VISCOUNT LOCKED HIMSELF UP INSIDE THE KEEP, CAUSING CONCERN FOR MY PARTISANS AS FAR AS LE MANS.

I ATTACKED HIM. IN VAIN...

OUR FIRST ATTACK HAS FAILED! BEAUMONT IS STANDING UP TO ME!

AS WAS MY HABIT, I GAVE UP ON ANY FURTHER ATTACK AND BLOCKED THE CITY!

FAMINE WILL BEAT THEM! THEIR KEEP WILL NOT DERIDE US MUCH LONGER!

FROM THEN ON, I BESIEGED THE CASTLE.

LET US ESTABLISH ENTRENCHED CAMPS IN THE BEUGIC VALLEY TO HOUSE THE TROOPS!

SOON, NEWS WAS TO DRAG ME AWAY FROM THE SIEGE. AS CAEN WAS SUFFERING A PLAGUE EPIDEMIC, MY DEAR WIFE, AT THE AGE OF FIFTY, FELL ILL LATE SUMMER...

WILLIAM, I HAVE SAD NEWS.

MATILDA ...

MATILDA PASSED ON AFTER THE FIRST HOUR THIS MORNING!

SAD FIRST OF NOVEMBER...

I PLACED A FAITHFUL CAPTAIN, ALAN RUFUS, IN CHARGE OF THE ROYAL ARMY BEFORE RETURNING TO CAEN.

MATILDA, MATILDA...

ON THE 3RD OF NOVEMBER, MY POOR QUEEN WAS BURIED IN THE CHOIR OF THE BENEDICTINE ABBEY IN CAEN.

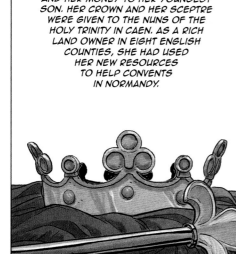

MATILDA LEFT ALL HER ENGLISH LAND AND HER MONEY TO HER YOUNGEST SON. HER CROWN AND HER SCEPTRE WERE GIVEN TO THE NUNS OF THE HOLY TRINITY IN CAEN. AS A RICH LAND OWNER IN EIGHT ENGLISH COUNTIES, SHE HAD USED HER NEW RESOURCES TO HELP CONVENTS IN NORMANDY.

IN 1083, I HAD LOST MY ONLY AND MY YOUNGER SISTER ADELAIDE, MY LAST BLOOD RELATION FROM MY MOTHER AND MY FATHER.

AFTER LIVING A MONASTIC LIFE IN 1077, MY DAUGHTER ADELA FINALLY MARRIED STEPHEN HENRY, COUNT OF BLOIS, CHARTRES AND MEAUX, IN 1084, TAKING PART IN THE ADMINISTRATION OF HER HUSBAND'S PRINCIPALITY.

IT WAS IN GLOUCESTER, ON THE 25TH OF DECEMBER 1085, THAT I ORDERED FOR AN EXCEPTIONAL SURVEY OF MY KINGDOM TO BE COMPILED, IN THE FORM OF THE "DOMESDAY BOOK".[16]

THE COST OF MILITARY CAMPAIGNS, THE RECESSION AND THE CHANGES IN HANDS OF MANY PROPERTIES WARRANTED SUCH CLARIFICATION!

THIS LONG SURVEY, SUPERVISED BY THE BISHOP OF DURHAM, WAS THE RESULT OF LOCAL ENQUIRIES THROUGHOUT HALF OF THE KINGDOM. THEY WERE ENDORSED AND COMPLETED BY ASSEMBLIES.

AS SOON AS IT WAS COMPLETE, TWO YEARS LATER, THIS BOOK ENABLED ME TO FISCALLY CONTROL ENGLAND VIA A RIGOROUS LAND REGISTRY, ACCOUNTING FOR PROPERTIES IN TERMS OF THEIR INHABITANTS, NATURE, SURFACE AND ASSOCIATED SERVICES.

IMPOSED AS THE NEW RULING CASTE, AN INFINITELY SMALL NORMAN ARISTOCRACY POSSESSED HALF OF THE KINGDOM.

ONLY TWO ENGLISHMEN STILL OWNED LARGE PROPERTIES...

THE DESPOILMENT OF THE ENGLISH NOBLEMEN KILLED AT HASTINGS AND STAMFORD BRIDGE, AND OF THEIR HEIRS, HAD ENABLED ME TO RECRUIT AN ARMY AND TO IMPOSE UPON THEM MILITARY TASKS IN EXCHANGE FOR RENTED PROPERTIES.

BY CREATING 180 HONOURS, I HAD A RESERVOIR OF 5,000 KNIGHTS, AS WELL AS MY ENGLISH MERCENARIES AND MILITIAMEN, TO RAISE MY OST AND REPRESS REBELLIONS.

SEVENTEEN YEARS AFTER DEVASTATING THE NORTH, THIS POOR LAND REMAINED ABANDONED. IT IS TRUE THAT FAMINE HAD BEEN RIFE FOR 9 YEARS THERE...

[16] THIS "BOOK" WAS CALLED SO FOR IT WAS PRODUCED THANKS TO SURVEYS THAT WERE SO INQUISITIVE THAT THEY WERE A SHOCK TO THE POPULATION.

IN 1086, BACK IN SAINTE-SUZANNE, FAMINE WAS STILL AN UNKNOWN QUANTITY! AND FOR A VERY GOOD REASON: THE FORTIFIED CITY HAD ITS OWN WELL.

AH! AH! THE NORMANS ARE UNAWARE OF THE UNDERGROUND GALLERY!

DESPITE A FOUR-YEAR SIEGE, THE FORTRESS IS THE ONLY CASTLE I HAVE NEVER MANAGED TO CAPTURE!

I MUST BE GETTING OLD! LET'S NEGOTIATE!

I AM DISCOURAGED BY THE LOSS OF SO MANY FAITHFUL COMPANIONS, BY THE RANSOMS CLAIMED FOR CAPTURED LORDS!

I CONCEDE TO PARLEY WITH THAT DARING BEAUMONT!

INTELLIGENTLY, I OFFERED HIM A FRIENDLY WELCOME TO ENGLAND.

BUT I AM NO FOOL. MY DIFFICULTIES IN MAINE ARE THE RESULT OF SUPPORT FROM MY TWO MAIN ENEMIES, THE COUNT OF ANJOU, FULK LE RÉCHIN AND THE KING OF FRANCE, PHILIP I.

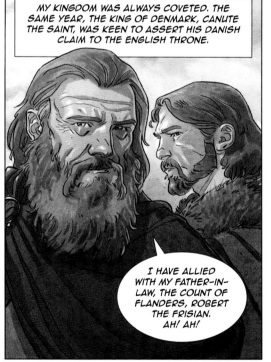

MY KINGDOM WAS ALWAYS COVETED. THE SAME YEAR, THE KING OF DENMARK, CANUTE THE SAINT, WAS KEEN TO ASSERT HIS DANISH CLAIM TO THE ENGLISH THRONE.

I HAVE ALLIED WITH MY FATHER-IN-LAW, THE COUNT OF FLANDERS, ROBERT THE FRISIAN. AH! AH!

AS YOU WELL KNOW HUBERT! UNDER MY REIGN, WAR BETWEEN MYSELF AND THE KING OF FRANCE IS A RECURRENT ISSUE.

I NEVERTHELESS GRANT YOU YOUR FATHER'S ESTATES AS A SIGN OF PEACE.

DURING AN ENCOUNTER IN KONGHELLE, THE OTHERWISE PACIFISTIC OLAF THE PEACEFUL, THE KING OF NORWAY, JOINED CANUTE'S PROJECT TO INVADE ...

AFTER THE PAST TWO DECADES, I HAVE REASONS TO BEAR A GRUDGE AGAINST WILLIAM: MY FATHER WAS KILLED AT STAMFORD BRIDGE!

HOWEVER, THE FISCAL COST OF OLAF'S FUTURE LANDING IN ENGLAND WAS UNPOPULAR.

THE PEOPLE OF JUTLAND REBELLED.

ON THE 10TH OF JULY 1086, HE WAS ASSASSINATED THERE, ALONG WITH 17 MEN FROM HIS PRIVATE GUARD.

AHH!!

AFTER REUNITING A FLEET IN A DANISH FJORD, HE SOUGHT REFUGE IN A CHURCH IN ODENSE.

HE HAD FAILED TO BRING HIS ENGLISH PLANS TO FRUITION

AND HIS WIFE, ADELA, RETURNED TO FLANDERS WITH THEIR SON! HIS DEATH PUT AN END TO THE CONSPIRACY HE HAD DEVISED WITH ROBERT.

IN SALISBURY, ON THE FIRST DAY OF AUGUST 1086...

MY VASSALS, I HAVE BROUGHT THE NORMAN FEUDAL SYSTEM IN LINE WITH THE KEY PRINCIPLES OF ANGLO-SAXON LAW...

...IN RESPECT OF YOUR REGIONAL CUSTOMS, WHILST INTRODUCING RELIGIOUS COURTS.

I NOW DECLARE THE MAINTENANCE OF THE LAWS OF MY PREDECESSOR, AND OF THOSE I HAVE PERSONALLY DECREED, FOR THE GOOD OF THE ENGLISH PEOPLE!

I CONSIDERED THEIR SERMON AS AN ESSENTIAL REMINDER, IN A PERIOD OF UNCERTAINTY.

THE 170 VASSALS SWORE THEIR ALLEGIANCE PROVIDED THAT THEY NOT BE CHEATED.

THEN, AT PEACE, I SPENT MY LAST MONTHS IN NORMANDY.

AT THE DOORWAY TO HEAVEN, THE DAY OF ATONEMENT

I recently fell ill in Rouen. Now, in August 1087, I am obese, I must confess. Ah! The King of France can mock indeed, he who is as fat as I am, "When will that fat fellow be confined?" he said. But, by the glory of God, I shall go and be churched in Notre-Dame in Paris and I shall bring one hundred thousand candles to the Kingdom of France against which I must continue to wage war!

In the past, King Henry had granted the Vexin county to my father. Upon the death of the last Count of Vexin in 1082, the territory passed on to France. And I have claimed it ever since! Again and again! This very month, I shall engage in combat against Philip I. Oh! This brief campaign took my ost to Mantes! I bathed the city in blood and fire! The old conquering demon of my ancestors who once pillaged the Seine! I still have Old Norse blood in me! Oh, I can hear those poisonous tongues, "It's the potbellied duke-king's last combat against the king who is still allied to his eldest son!" Others claimed that my secret dream was to snatch France! I could well have nourished such desire today, had a nasty wound not prevented me! In Mantes, I was seriously injured in the stomach, suffocating in the stifling heat of the fire. Very probably ruptured liver or spleen...

Over the past few days, I have been agonising, bedridden, in the Priory of St. Gervais near Rouen. But perfectly clear-headed. Did I not come here to tell you of my reign? Just the time to dictate, before notaries, the details of my succession for my three sons, Robert, William and Henry, and I will soon be gone. I ask again that my treasures be divided between my sons and ecclesiastical institutions. I forgive my eldest son Robert, even if he refuses to come to my death bed, whilst partially disinheriting him. I admit that it was my earlier intention to totally disinherit him. But the barons discouraged me.

On the contrary, my half-brother Robert has failed to obtain my pardon for his brother Odo, imprisoned for the past seven years for rebellion. Nevertheless! He has obtained his release. I also order for all prisoners who promise not to disturb public order to be released. You can therefore set the obstinate rebel Count Morcar free. But... Roger de Breteil, the Earl of Hereford, imprisoned since his 1075 revolt, may not be set free! My resentment against him remains steadfast. One Easter Day, I had precious garments taken to him in prison. He had them burned!

On this morning of Thursday 9th September, I feel my hour is approaching. Don't say a word, I know. Don't look at me that way, my friend. It is but poor William who is departing. But? Tell me, my faithful Henry, what is that tinkling in the distance? Could it be the cathedral bells ringing... Yes... the cathedral... The cath... There in the distance. So far away already... I commend myself to the mother of God. May she reconcile me with her son...

Such were his last words.

The sun appeared twenty-one times in the sign of Virgo on this 9th of September 1087. William was 60 years old. The King of England is no longer, after a reign of twenty years, ten months and a handful of days. He is dead, and from now on, he is as if abandoned by family and people. Yet he has left behind six orphans, three of them girls, Cecilia, Constance and Adela.

Immediately, they were all stricken with grief. Rich courtiers rode to their homes to ensure their goods were put in safe place. During their masters' absence, servants snatched William's goods – clothing, vases, linen, furniture – before, in turn, taking to their heels. Only the Rouen clergy paid the last honours to his despoiled remains. For two hours, from prime to terce, the king lay virtually naked on the floor. Two terrible hours for he who personified Normandy's magnificence.

Only one grateful knight, Herluin, hired embalmers, at his own cost, and arranged the duke-king's funeral in the abbey church of St. Stephen in Caen. Once his heavy and stocky body had been sown inside a cow's hide, Herluin accompanied the hearse to William's final resting place. Unloaded on the banks of the River Orne, the knight's troubles were still not over. As the crown and the abbot of the church of St. Stephen headed towards William's mortal remains, a fire broke out in the city. There was an immediate wave of panic. As the fire ravaged through half of the town, the monks continued the ceremony, alone, accompanying William to the abbey-church and singing psalms.

Just like Matilda's funeral four years previously, he was laid to rest before the grand altar. Only one of his sons attended, worthy Henry, and among the prelates and barons, Geoffrey de Montbray in particular. A sad ending! Haro! Haro[17]! This cry of justice sounded the end of the ceremony. It was made by a certain Ascelin. Before the king's grave, he dared to claim his due: the land upon which the abbey-church was built had never been paid to his father! The bishops immediately paid the requested sum, enabling calm to be restored for the Conqueror's burial.

As soon as he learned of his father's death, Robert returned to Normandy, introducing himself as the Duke of Normandy and Count of Maine, furious with his younger brother who had often paid homage to him as their father's heir…

The agonising king had sent his loyal son William to England, to accede to the throne. The latter embarked in the royal port of Touques, sailed to the English coast then headed for Winchester to join his former tutor Lanfranc, who abided by the Conqueror's wishes: his successor William Rufus was crowned in Westminster on the following 26th of September, in the same abbey where the Conqueror had been consecrated two decades previously. His younger son's reign was marked by a struggle for Normandy and England with his eldest son Robert. Not forgetting his mischievous son Henry, the youngest and who was torn between the rivalry of his elders, to whom William, in his last hours of agony, had bequeathed a fortune in silver pounds… But that's a different story…

[17] Legal cry made by the victim of a crime and that obliges officials to intervene.

WILLIAM

CHRONOLOGICAL AND HISTORIC REFERENCES

WILLIAM
THE FIRST DUKES OF NORMANDY

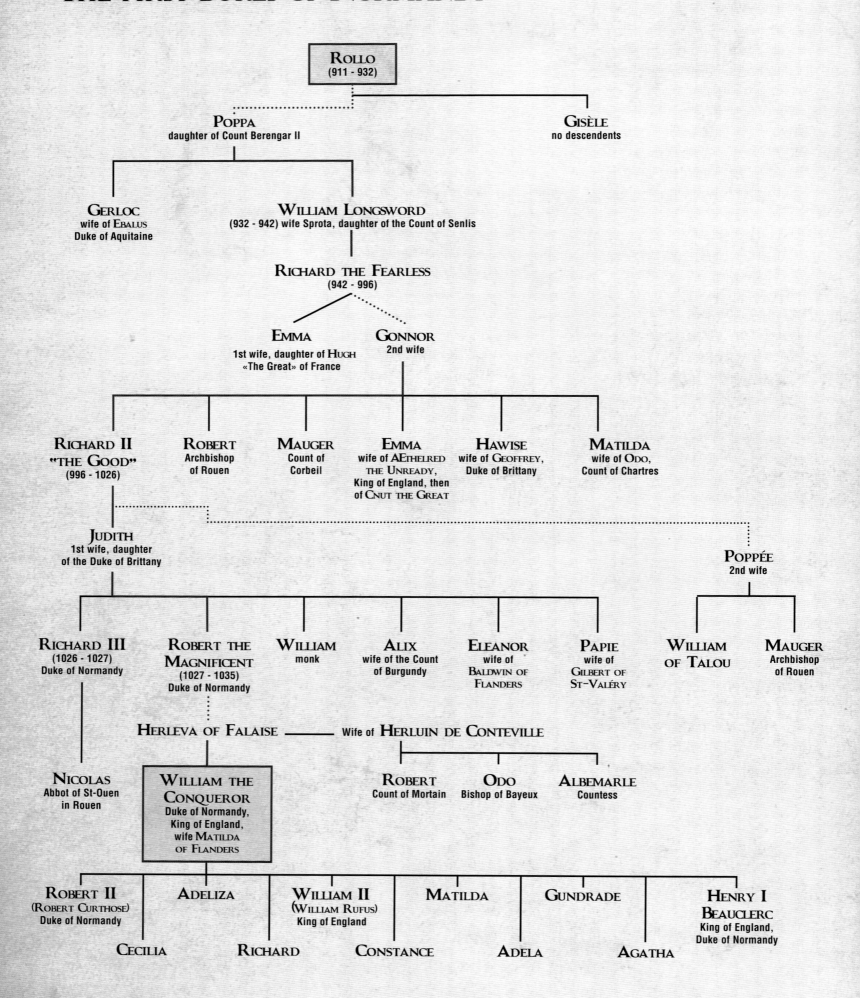

ROLLO
(911 - 932)

POPPA
daughter of Count Berengar II

GISÈLE
no descendents

GERLOC
wife of EBALUS
Duke of Aquitaine

WILLIAM LONGSWORD
(932 - 942) wife Sprota, daughter of the Count of Senlis

RICHARD THE FEARLESS
(942 - 996)

EMMA
1st wife, daughter of HUGH
«The Great» of France

GONNOR
2nd wife

**RICHARD II
"THE GOOD"**
(996 - 1026)

ROBERT
Archbishop
of Rouen

MAUGER
Count of
Corbeil

EMMA
wife of AETHELRED
THE UNREADY,
King of England, then
of CNUT THE GREAT

HAWISE
wife of GEOFFREY,
Duke of Brittany

MATILDA
wife of ODO,
Count of Chartres

JUDITH
1st wife, daughter
of the Duke of Brittany

POPPÉE
2nd wife

RICHARD III
(1026 - 1027)
Duke of Normandy

**ROBERT THE
MAGNIFICENT**
(1027 - 1035)
Duke of Normandy

WILLIAM
monk

ALIX
wife of the Count
of Burgundy

ELEANOR
wife of
BALDWIN OF
FLANDERS

PAPIE
wife of
GILBERT OF
ST-VALÉRY

**WILLIAM
OF TALOU**

MAUGER
Archbishop
of Rouen

HERLEVA OF FALAISE —————— Wife of **HERLUIN DE CONTEVILLE**

NICOLAS
Abbot of St-Ouen
in Rouen

**WILLIAM THE
CONQUEROR**
Duke of Normandy,
King of England,
wife MATILDA
OF FLANDERS

ROBERT
Count of Mortain

ODO
Bishop of Bayeux

ALBEMARLE
Countess

ROBERT II
(ROBERT CURTHOSE)
Duke of Normandy

ADELIZA

WILLIAM II
(WILLIAM RUFUS)
King of England

MATILDA

GUNDRADE

**HENRY I
BEAUCLERC**
King of England,
Duke of Normandy

CECILIA

RICHARD

CONSTANCE

ADELA

AGATHA

WILLIAM
THE NORMAN CONQUEST OF ENGLAND, 1066-1068

VIKING STATES

KINGDOM OF SCOTLAND

EDINBURGH

NORTHUMBRIA

STAMFORD BRIDGE
Harold's victory over the King of Norway (25th September 1066)

YORK

TERRITORY OF DUBLIN

DUBLIN

LINCOLN

IRELAND

SHREWSBURY

KINGDOM OF ENGLAND

WALES

LONDON

WINDSOR

CANTERBURY

EXETER

HASTINGS
William the Conqueror's victory over Harold (14th October 1066)

St-Valéry-sur-Somme

BARFLEUR

FÉCAMP

LILLEBONNE

DIVES

ROUEN

DUCHY OF NORMANDY

BAYEUX

CAEN

COUTANCES

FALAISE

EXMES

MONT-SAINT-MICHEL

BRITTANY

KINGDOM OF FRANCE

CAPTION

- ▬ William the Conqueror's Norman fleet (1066)
- ▬ Norwegians
- ☆ Main battles
- ➤ Harold, King of England's march (1066)
- ★ Uprisings (1066-1068)

WILLIAM
HIS LEGACY IN NORMANDY

THE BAYEUX TAPESTRY

For a long time referred to as «Queen Matilda's Tapestry», the Bayeux Tapestry is in fact a woollen embroidery on a strip of linen around 70 metres long.

Kept in the town's cathedral up to the 18th century, it was very probably commissioned to an English embroidery workshop, shortly after the conquest of England in 1066, by Bishop Odo of Conteville, William, Duke of Normandy's half brother.

Today, the Bayeux Tapestry offers a precious testimony to the Conquest of England and to this eventful period in history. It is listed on UNESCO's Memory of the World Register.

FALAISE

Robert, who became Duke of Normandy upon the death of his brother Richard III, met Herleva, a young girl whose father was a tanner in Falaise; he fell helplessly in love and took her to live in his castle. A few months later, William was born from their union. Their union was illegitimate, for Herleva was not a member of the Norman nobility, and was soon to be contested by the powerful Norman barons, who also descended from dukes. Herleva, also known as Arlette, became the Duke of Normandy's official concubine, his «frilla» according to «more danico» tradition, i.e. the Danish tradition practiced by the Dukes of Normandy and by which they had their mistresses take up residence within their courts, even if they were already married by the Church. Robert is known to have taken no other wife than Herleva.

Falaise Castle.

DIVES-SUR-MER

It was in Dives that William gathered his fleet and his army to conquer the throne of England, usurped by Harold upon Edward's death. For over six months, he built an impressive armada of ships that transported 3,000 horses, over 12,000 warriors, weapons and provisions. The order to leave for England was given on the 9th of September 1066.

Mouth of the River Dives

BAYEUX

It is very probably in this town, whose bishop since 1049 was Odo - the son of Herleva and Herluin de Conteville - that William had the Saxon Harold publicly swear upon holy relics that he would let him succeed to the throne of England.

Bayeux Cathedral.

CAEN

This small market town, mentioned in 1027 in a charter by Richard III, was, thanks to William, to become an important city with a fortified castle, the Men's Abbey and the Ladies' Abbey. The latter was consecrated on the 18th of June 1066, shortly before the conquest. William and Matilda offered their daughter Cecilia in oblation to the abbey dedicated to the Holy Trinity.

Caen Castle.

Facade of the Holy Trinity abbey-church. Ladies' Abbey.

Apse of the abbey-church of St. Stephen. Men's Abbey.

WILLIAM
HIS LEGACY IN NORMANDY (continued)

MONTIVILLIERS

Robert the Magnificent, occasionally referred to as «the Liberal» due to his great generosity towards the Church, was keen to seek pardon for the acts of violence committed against members of the religious order during his adolescence. The Abbey of Montivilliers, founded by St. Philibert in 684, is a case in point. Pillaged by the Scandinavians in the 9th century, the duke granted the abbey its independence via a charter dating from January 1035, whilst concurrently endowing the establishment with generous donations.

The Abbey of Montivilliers chapter house, displaying the Rule of St. Benedict.

LE BEC-HELLOUIN

Bec Abbey was founded by Herluin, a vassal to the Count of Brionne, in 1034. The abbey acquired a reputation that stretched well beyond the frontiers of Normandy and attracted Lanfranc de Pavie, who became its prior. William, who had supported the siege of Brionne, just three leagues from Le Bec, finally met with Lanfranc who he had forced into exile for being insolent with one of his soldiers. Lanfranc kept his composure before the duke, who was impressed by the abbot's self-assurance and forthrightness. William took him back to the abbey with great pomp, hence marking the dawn of a great friendship between the two men.

Ruins of Bec Abbey.

ST-WANDRILLE-RANÇON

The Abbey of Fontenelle, founded by Wandrille in 649, was pillaged several times by Scandinavians. Duke Richard I had it rebuilt from its ruins in 960. William and Matilda, protectors of the Church, endowed this abbey with many riches.

Ruins of the Abbey of St. Wandrille

FÉCAMP

It was in Fécamp, on the 8th of April 1067, on Easter Sunday that King William chose to celebrate his return to Normandy. He was offered a triumphant welcome, as were his companions, who were stitched in gold from head to foot.

Ruins of the ducal palace.   Abbey-church.

ROUEN

The duke-king's condition continued to worsen after his accident in Mantes. He was taken to his palace in Rouen, then to the Priory of St. Gervais. After six months of agony, William the Conqueror, his faithful son Henry by his side, gave his last breath on the morning of the 9th of September 1087. His body was transported by boat to Caen where he was buried in the choir of the abbey-church of St. Stephen.

ICI ÉTAIT
LE PRIEURÉ DE SAINT GERVAIS
OÙ MOURUT
GUILLAUME LE CONQUÉRANT
LE IX SEPTEMBRE
MLXXXVII

ACADEMIA ROTH. POSUIT AN· MDCCCXLVI

The Priory of St. Gervais where the body of William the Conqueror lay before his burial.